BWR

BLACK WARRIOR REVIEW

Black Warrior Review is named after the river that borders the campus of The University of Alabama in Tuscaloosa. The city, river, and journal derive their names from the sixteenth-century Indian chief Tuscaloosa, whose name comes from two words of Creek or Choctaw origin—*tusca* (warrior) and *lusa* (black).

*

Black Warrior Review is published semiannually at The University of Alabama. Subscriptions are $16 per year + $6 for Canadian and foreign subscriptions. Make checks payable to The University of Alabama or shop online at http://bwr.ua.edu.

Manuscripts are read year round. Complete submission guidelines are available online.

Black Warrior Review is indexed in the Humanities International Complete, the Book Reviews Index, and the MLA International Bibliography.

All correspondence to
Box 862936
Tuscaloosa, Alabama 35486

http://bwr.ua.edu
bwr@ua.edu

ISSN: 0193-6301

Printed by Creasey Printing Services.

BLACK WARRIOR REVIEW
FALL/WINTER 2011   ISSUE 38.1

EDITOR
Farren Stanley

FICTION/PROSE EDITOR
Danilo John Thomas

MANAGING EDITOR
Emma Sovich

NONFICTION EDITOR
Tessa Fontaine

DESIGN EDITOR
Betsy Seymour

POETRY EDITOR
AB Gorham

ASSISTANT FICTION/PROSE EDITORS
Tom Cotsonas, Dara K. Ewing, Devin Gribbons, Katy Gunn, Juan Carlos
Reyes, Jessica Richardson, Ben Stroud, Lisa Tallin, Brandi Wells

ASSISTANT NONFICTION EDITORS
Annie Agnone, Freya Gibbon, Barry Grass, Katy Gunn, Laura Kochman,
Paige McCormick, Juan Carlos Reyes, Lisa Tallin

ASSISTANT POETRY EDITORS
Annie Agnone, Anne Brettell, Dara K. Ewing, Pia Simone Garber,
Katy Gunn, Joshua R. Helms, Eric Karin, Kristen Kuczenski, Caroline
Klocksiem, Laura Kochman, Matthew Mahaney, Jason McCall, Lisa Tallin

EDITORIAL ASSISTANTS
Christel Chappell, Freya Gibbon, Katy Gunn, Kayla Hare, Laura Kochman,
Cassandra Mahaffey, Mary Martin, Brandi Wells

COVER   Helen Pynor, "Liquid Ground I," 2011

FEATURE COVER   Helen Pynor, "Thames I," 2010

CHAPBOOK COVER   AB Gorham

Contents

FEATURE

JA Tyler

[the fifth house]

I built a fifth house near the river. I placed my head under its water and drank. I was a deer again, as my brother and I had been when we were young, when we had antlers, when we lowered our necks. My brother the deer, that forest. We would run in those woods until the sun dissolved, until the river froze. Those were different woods than these.

In these woods, standing beside this river, I am lost. I don't know where I came from. I left a trail of yarn, what was a scarf, but when I follow it, I am only led in circles. I loop trees and rocks but don't come to any understanding. These woods are where I am going to die. When my brother and I were deer, those were the woods of our beginnings.

I built this fifth house of scarf yarn, layering it up into walls and windows. I worked the yarn as a constructivist would. I built a chimney for the first snow and hung gutters for the rain. I planted flowers in the front to greet my brother when he returns, when he brings a scythe instead of a black dot on a scrap of paper, when he brings intention. And if he never does, the flowers will burn up like summer, my scarf yarn to flames in front of this house.

I have a knife, and it will be here with these flowers, ahead of our next brother-moment.

I wait for my brother to return with hooves, though he may hide inside of a fox or a bear or a rabbit. He may linger in a bird until it is time. He may scramble up my roof in a squirrel body, in the grass with a snake skin, strong with the jaw of a mountain lion. From my open doorway, twirling a strung-out wall of yarn in my fingers, I am a careful eye on these trees. These woods will not abandon me, even though I am lost, even though my brother is hiding in its furs, even though the moment of my death has been brought to me here, wrapped in trees.

In these woods, there is only death and coming-death. There is no living.

I have skinned or burned all of these animals. They are not my brothers, and what I am looking for inside of them is buried deep. The yarn-house, this fifth house, it led me in circles until I was back and inside of myself, unsure about everything. And the darkness there, inside of these last moments of being, as we die, they are torment. The burning down of these houses, it is imperative, and it is the only comfort we find. When we are dying, there is no other way to exist.

In these woods is a history.

In these woods is how history opens up inside of us.

My brother came. My brother handed me a note. The note did not have words. The note was a shape. The shape was a circle. The circle was black. This was a dot on paper. This was how my brother, in his handing me a message, told me that I was dying.

I was in these woods, hiding or trying to get out. I had only these deer-memories.

My brother stood next to me. His deer-face breathing. I said I don't want this but his deer-head was silent and the forest bloomed in front of me. One step and his buck-white tail was all I saw, this immaculate disappearance. Those were these woods, where I would never end. That was my deer-brother cleaning me out of being. That was the last memory of having been, before having not, and how the running in the woods felt, the two of us boys as deer, and the river alongside.

My fifth house was a house of scarf-yarn, without a note of winter. My fifth house was where I watched the tree-line, waiting for brother-return. My fifth house was about looping, following yarn-line into a forest, finding myself lost in deathly aperture.

The message found me, this brother-delivered death. I refuse to believe it.

I write back, profound in this loss.

Dear Woods: why did you open your mouth so wide? There were pine needles on the floor and it scared me. What does it take to perform that kind of magic? I've learned that beneath those woods, where your roots are buried, there is something called permafrost, a cold that never shrinks, and that is more frightening than your open mouth or your yawn. What you say might temper this, but I am a mountain of doubt. I'll keep walking even if it is only in circles, in these woods, until nothing scares me anymore.

In these woods, between a tree and these deer, there is my death.

In these woods, a fifth house, built on the shreds of living left hung about my neck.

Dear Death: what do you have to gain from all of this?

I spark a fire, and it grows.

As deer we breathed woods, my brother and I. We ran through lifetimes. A river is generous in its running. A moon rises even as my fifth house burns. This fifth house flames up and I am on the rug of yarn, in a bed of yarn, underneath a roof of yarn. Animals scatter back to their homes in the branches and the hollows. This fifth house, this scarf-yarn house, goes quickly burning down, and I am alone.

In these woods, it is only about learning how to remember our deer-brother.

Dear Brother: remember, there are always still these woods.

DEREK GROMADZKI

Sooth

Long place,   this. Under-welkin where
                  boughs corse knots and there is stroth,
and strothmen's heads tilt balded angle. And rede, of wayfare
and way of ware.
        Could lour near an inward song
                  to gode all grief forget;
allay the count of foundlings.   Been
places floors crept terrors.
        A sing that   cannot stay rote motion
                 'less wrap your hollows in a heap.
       Abode the warmth offerings offered
                ald again when I am cleave. Skull,
        be dogbone when I go unsaid.
    To mouth that speak that leads
   not to searching
       but unto seeks.

Quarter

By, where glade gives on   glades-give open onto unroll
   marsh. Sinks progress start more and moors   slow   as   slumber.
        Brace. Let back a sinister of bites and stings.
  Silence about the space of twice two days for draft.
    Below thatch-beam. We footprint here soft weakened gaits
         with waterskins dead weight for water.
    There was sat down on me a stillness.
Quiet witness to favor...so still.
      But making in already moves—
         straggling-tugs us wights up by our trample.
    Feign I, into weal and run ablur of sturdy.

Joelle Biele

Poppies

Back past the crumbling buildings with their cellars of coal, night chimneys, and peeling paint, past stairwells and once-gilded rails, flowers with rusting leaves, back past the soot and the cars, the trams crossing the street and down the road that once knew trucks and tanks and machinery heavier than this, if you follow that road you will find a gas station with its requisite attendant smoking a cigarette, and if you look behind him, you will see a gate that's not really a gate into a park, that's not really a park, that is still grand to those who want to remember and to those who want to forget, where once, when they were children, their neighbors were asked to dig their own graves. If you walk down the path to the field, the one on the right, past poppy stems bending under the weight of drowsy pods and tiny seeds, you will find a boy named Timosz, or Timoteusz, to be exact, since that is his given name and the name of his grandfather who disappeared into the mountains leaving his grandmother, as the story must go, alone, and Timosz, with all the precision of a boy hoping to make it big in big time sports, soccer or hockey, he hasn't decided, Timosz kicks the ball at the sun, but he is too late, the sun is what he wanted, not the hills or the grass or the yellow weeds, and not his father, who can juggle the ball with his knees and wants to get home and put on his slippers and watch some TV. His father kicks the ball to his once-beaming boy so he can think he did the right thing. His son has lost interest in the game and is not sure when he will try again. He smiles politely, is ready to go home, and though he no longer beams at the sky and stares at the ground, he is still, at this moment, his father's boy to behold.

*

After his mother whispers that the man in the hat is an imposter, he is not really a ticket-inspector but a thief riding the tram, after holding his mother's hand, his mother, who he will later understand aged too fast, that life in a small apartment was too much, that she never should have

followed his father from their village under the pines, who wants Timosz
to learn to dance so she has made him a billowing shirt and billowing
pants to fill like sails when he spins behind a row of spinning girls and
has embroidered a vest and belt with flowers, which he likes because he
can pretend he is a soldier, and the belt holds his sword, and he is a rider
heading into battle and not a boy trying to learn to dance, but a boy who
would rather be reading comic books instead. They get off the tram beside
a field where the faithful once prayed and a shallow stream feeds into a
ruined river where men come to fight after too much vodka and beer,
and too much soccer, re-enacting some ancient play that goes back before
soccer, before horses and wide and blowing plains, and after Timosz and
his mother cross the grassy tracks and enter the park in this battered jewel
of a city with its cafés, mechanical cars, planes, and rocket ships, Timosz,
who wonders why some cartoons are dubbed with the voice of only one
man, kicks the ball hard, harder than he meant, because why can't there
be more than one man, one for the Viking, one for the amorous shark,
and one for the singing Italian who somehow got on board; Timosz, who
thinks when he grows up and rules the world or a small television station,
that he will make sure there is more than one man reading the script,
there will be more than one script so no one has to share, and after he
is done recording the story the world will know that Timosz the Great
was right, that there should be more than one man, more than one tram,
comics for everyone, and more than one ball for children to kick into the
eye of the sun.

*

Timosz, who draws pictures of himself, sometimes with pencil,
sometimes with pen, sometimes in full color with a tin of broken crayons
while sitting at the kitchen table, or lying on the floor, or on the back of
a worksheet at school, draws pictures that everyone will admire for their
attention to detail, especially the players' positions in a stadium where
everyone chants "Ti-mosz! Ti-mosz!" after his friend, fellow soccer star
Adam, throws him the ball under the humming lights so he can dribble
towards his nemesis from school, Jakub who is called Kuba, who always

has new sneakers that his mother buys at the mall, who likes to show them off and prop his feet on his desk when the teacher is out of the room, and who is now goalie, famous, but not as famous as Timosz, and known for being very good at his job because he is exceptionally quick and tall, and, most importantly, because he is not afraid to be hit in the face by anyone or anything. Everyone chants "Ti-mosz! Ti-mosz!" and Kuba looks like the shark Timosz always knew he was, and Timosz kicks the ball just out of Kuba's reach and the announcer and the entire stadium let out one long "GOAAAAALLLL!" at which point Timosz is proud of his drawing and wants to show his mother, who is too busy to look. If you look through the window you will see how she looks away and says the picture is nice, she will look at it later though Timosz knows she will not, she will forget as she always does. So, he looks at his father who is lost in the paper. Timosz knows it is better not to disturb him at such times, so he offers the picture to his mother as a gift which gets her to lean down and give him a kiss, give the picture a look. Timosz hopes she will notice the effort he put into the crowd, the individual faces, even the sun with its angled rays, hopes she will notice there are no empty seats because the whole town comes each week to see him play and despairs over his slightest injury. She looks at the picture a second, then at her husband a second longer, and thanks her son, strokes the back of his head almost the way she used to and puts the picture on top of the mail, and tells him to get washed, to get ready for dinner. It is almost time to eat.

*

Outside the apartment, in the courtyard of his building, Timosz kicks the ball under the careful eye of Mrs. X, who stands on her balcony the whole time he plays, making sure the ball does not roll anywhere near the newly-installed azaleas, or her potted stonecrop, or the rhododendrons the building committee purchased with great care and serious bargaining with one of the tenants' cousins at a nursery in town. She stands there with her roughly-dyed hair and wonders why he is not at the park, it is such a beautiful day, surely there is more space so why doesn't he take the tram and find some children to play? She does not say this aloud, she does not want to be friendly, she is hoping she can get Timosz to leave with her scowl, which only confuses Timosz because her husband, who smiles and waves from the window, likes to talk about how he played soccer before the war, how he spent part of the war in England. What neither Mrs. X nor her husband, nor their orchids leaning against the window, know is that Timosz would rather be at the park, too. Timosz does not know what has happened between his parents, he does not wonder if all parents are like this, he assumes they are, and he does not know that his mother resents his father because he did not want another child, or that his father resents the fact that he cannot buy her the ring she wants and resents her for wanting it, so he is sure to be first to make a toast or break into song at tables in winter heavy with food, in summer set under the trees. No one suspects his long silence. When he goes out, no one knows where, he tells his wife and son he needs copper wire one millimeter thick so he can listen to Mozart on Sunday. His search may go on for days until he is ready to be with his family again. This particular morning they have sent Timosz into the courtyard with his ball, not so they can lie down the way they used to, but so his father can take apart the stereo, and his mother can make honey cake with raspberries and soft white cheese so that she can invite her husband to join her for coffee and sweets and maybe catch a glimpse of who he once was. Their story may or may not be Timosz's future but it is all right because Timosz is outside kicking the ball against the wall. Mrs. X has given up, or maybe gone for tea so she can watch him all over again, and as Timosz kicks the ball he is thinking of dragons in this city of dragons, of real and imaginary dragons, dragons under the castle and in the town square, toy dragons with and without hats, dragons made out of plush, dragons made out of wood, dragons on keychains and dragons on shirts, and Timosz is thinking how he could defeat the star of the city team in a head-to-head match or series of penalty kicks because he can outrun fire and wings and they will play all-or-nothing in the field now greening beyond the city's second ring.

*

Timosz, whose father will not let him hold the umbrella, won't let him try, though, Timosz is sure he could hold it high enough not to hit his father's head and explains this to his father carefully, with reasonable enough logic, decides that when he grows up, when he is a father, he will let his children hold the umbrella. They will have their own umbrellas, and candy, and when they ask for a toy at the kiosk window, they will get it, instead of having to resort to various forms of manipulation that never work. Timosz gets into the tram with his father because it is too wet to play. The sun is impossible to locate, and he hopes his father will regale him with tales of famous players and legendary matches and they can go over their favorite TV moments from the World Cup, which was the longest Timosz had ever spent alone with his father, and after which his father bought him this small blue ball, with a World Cup logo and two dragons chasing each other's tails. The tram runs by what once was the ghetto, and by a graveyard that was plowed into a parking lot, though, Timosz does not know this. He looks out the window and sees the town square where music floats down from the tower, the trumpeter playing every hour on the hour, who between hours sleeps, or eats, or reads a magazine, no one knows what, maybe watching from the small window people climbing the statue, or feeding the birds, wondering why people delight in feeding those filthy birds unless they think they are their beautiful dead and can thereby gain a glimpse of the afterlife, but if they are the afterlife he wants none of it. Poppies will not bring them back. The poppies will not grow. From his perch, the trumpeter notes to himself how tourists walk by the long-gone stain where a protestor set himself on fire and the wall where names were posted so people could be called in, but Timosz does not see what the trumpeter sees. He only sees his father, who spent his boyhood trying to catch the exact moment the mountain snow crashed into the streams and water went whooshing through town, who spent his mornings listening for birds so he could bring them home for the proverbial stew, his father who wants him to get good grades so he can go to university and doesn't understand why Timosz wants to be a glazier like him, carrying giant plates of glass through the streets. The reason is that his son wants to look through glass and see pictures perfectly framed, though he cannot put it that way, he may never put it that way, but then they get off the tram to get back to his mother who is inside the apartment sweeping, and there we see them turning the corner, Timosz asking his father if just once, this once, he can kick the ball down the leaf-splattered street slick with rain.

BRANDON DAVIS JENNINGS

Operation Toe Breaker

Here's a real war story. Sergeant Dowd broke Matt Demaray's foot so Matt wouldn't have to go to the desert. He was tagged to deploy and watch Third Country Nationals clean port-o-johns in an undisclosed location. That's a job that should scare no one, a job that should bore everyone, and most importantly, a job that must be done.

—That's not artful.

—Because it isn't art.

—Then you better make it so.

The summer of 2000, before I joined the Air Force, I moved back to California to do some real work after earning a 0.67 GPA at Concord College in West Virginia; the only work I did was sleep all day and drink all night. One night, at some girl's apartment in Lancaster, a bunch of my friends and I were drinking and talking about the political ramifications of *The Snorks* or *Fraggle Rock,* and a guy I knew from high school started screaming about his sister: "She was my love," he'd yelled. Something close to that. I did not have a tape recorder.

He'd finished Marine boot camp a few days earlier and was on leave. Marine boot camp, in my opinion, is a serious thing. I completed most of Air Force Basic Training with my BCGs stowed in my cargo pocket. It was no harder to fold creases into the elastic of my underwear or march in step with the trainee in front of me whether I had crisp vision or saw the world as mud. I'd like to believe that Marines need to complete tasks in Basic Training that nearly-blind men cannot; that is one way in which I distinguish Marines from Airmen. I've heard that Marines are also trained to be killers who see the things they kill.

—Some guys in the Air Force are trained for that.

—Others have to imagine the deaths they're responsible for.

—No one makes them imagine anything.

—No one prevents it either.

The New Marine was drunk and screaming about his love, whom, as stated earlier, was his sister. Why he used the past tense I doubt I'll ever know; she was alive then and is alive now. I walked out on the balcony and leaned over the hard, black railing. The New Marine sat on the sidewalk and smashed a hunk of pavement against his foot. He grunted and spat and made angry sounds with every blow. What he did not do was injure himself in a profound way.

—Should I describe the red-orange horizon and talk about the wax-paper moon in order to evoke the McCarthyesque?

—Cormac. Not General McCarthy, right?

—Right. Let's say Cormacesque for the sake of clarity.

—And you mean *Blood Meridian*. Not *The Road*.

—Indeed.

It was another *B.M.* Cormacesque Mojave Desert eve and, on the sidewalk below me, the New Marine repeatedly slammed a rock on his foot and screamed about his sister. She was his love, as I said before. This phrase meant something to him; I'm sure of it.

I was drunk at the time. That was one thing I was quite good at in my middle teens, and late teens and early twenties and middle twenties and late twenties. Soon I may be good at being drunk at thirty. That's not misguided bragging or a persona thing. I didn't read much until I started to care about writing. If I had, then I might have drank less to ensure I didn't "riff off" Bukowski and Thompson and Joyce and O'Brien and so on. But they riffed too, so when the riffing police ride into town on their peppermint horses, we're all gonna be fucked.

—What does that mean?

—You know exactly what it means.

The New Marine's unsuccessful self-destruction got on my nerves, and I'd had just about enough. I didn't go down there and confront him, of course. Someone else went down there, and I remember feeling relieved that he had. It's about time so-and-so went down there and took care of that nonsense, I thought, because if he hadn't, I might have marched down there and handled things myself, which is easy to say, and even easier to think, when there is no longer a possibility that you may have to act on your words or thoughts. Irritation mollified, I went inside and sat down on a couch next to a guy and girl who petted one another so fast that I feared they'd burst into flames and burn the apartment down.

—Objection. Relevance.

—It's a comment on public displays of lust.

—It's sustained stupidity.

I asked someone, "Where did the crazy guy go?"

Someone said, "To shoot himself in the foot."

—Did he shoot his foot?

—No idea. Never saw him again.

—What's the point then?

—She was his love, man.

*

There are a lot of ways to tell a war story. There's the *The Red Badge of Courage* way, and there's the *All Quiet on the Western Front* way. There is also the *Jarhead* way or the *Full Metal Jacket* way. For the philosophically inclined there's even Sun Tzu's *The Art of War* way, and although I agree with a lot of the stuff Ole Tzu said, I don't see any art in it.

—Then what the hell are you doing?

—This is pornography.

—What's art then?

—A mirror that refuses to show me my reflection after I've threatened to beat it senseless.

Slaughterhouse Five is pretty damn short as far as novels go. That's not a complaint; some novels aren't short enough. But Vonnegut's war story could've been told in two sentences. He was a miner in the first corpse mine. A man he knew vomited himself to death, and a guy was executed for stealing a teapot. This might have been about the length of my grandfather's war story had he not died of cancer before I had a chance to ask him about his time in the Pacific.

My grandfather joined the Navy when he was sixteen and rode a minesweeper to Hawaii. He was promoted to petty officer three times, and each time he strutted downtown to celebrate, he drank, was tattooed, and fought until the Military Police dragged him back to base where his new stripes were ripped off his sleeves. This might sound romantic, but my dad told me this, and Dad's a reliable source. Exempli gratia: I was the varsity quarterback for Desert High School my junior year, and one night, as Dad and I soaked in our second-hand hot tub and he tried to tease out a lesson from one of the numerous 0-63 shellackings I'd endured, he said, "You're too small to make it in professional sports." Dad was honest, and whether he was right or not at that moment, I never made it in professional sports. So he is right now, even if he wasn't supposed to be.

*

Real war stories aren't about excitement and adventure; they're about facts. Shitty, blood-caked facts and weakness, failure and cowardice, and most often boredom, ignorance, shame, and hatred. When heroism shows up in a war story it's probably told by someone who's never been to war or by someone who knows how to give an audience what it's hungry for.

—Which one are you?

—Both and neither.

—You're a cryptic asshole.

Hugh Martin, a friend and war-poet from Ohio, said that a section like this requires the mention of Tim O'Brien. I bought the First Mariner Books edition of *The Things They Carried* from Barnes & Noble; it was stacked on a table of nonfiction. There are two title pages; a book's quality is directly proportional to its number of title pages. The first title page looks like this:

The Things
They Carried

A Work of Fiction By
Tim O'Brien

I read this book of fiction/nonfiction when I was twenty-five and I hated it. I read it again when I was twenty-nine, and I know now that the reason I hated his book was that I was too immature to admit I was jealous of how simple it seemed for Timmy to communicate emotions with language.

*

This is a real war story. Adam Dowd was my swing-shift supervisor. He was a great friend, but he seemed depressed a lot of the time—perhaps the result of a divorce and psychological trauma inflicted by his ex-wife— I'm no psychologist. In my best effort to cheer him up, I talked shit to him. This worked for me in my childhood, so maybe I didn't know any better because I was a product of my environment. Maybe I liked being an asshole to a guy who would take it, especially one who outranked me.

Matt Demaray got popped for a TDY to the desert. He was one of the few people that I spent any off-duty time with. His deployment meant I was going to have fewer friends on base. Everyone else was lame. What was I going to do? Boo hoo, minced meat underwear, hamsters in nutcracker suits playing violins, and so on.

It was common practice to go to Matt's dorm room on lunch at midnight, or whenever we were off, and pop a few painkillers, then pound a couple beers before going back to sit at the console all night and play Xbox on a giant flat screen. (The TV was purchased with tax dollars that our higher-ups spent to ensure that our shop wouldn't get fewer tax dollars the next year.) On this particular night, we went to Matt's and Adam came along. Adam didn't care that we had a beer or two on our lunch break. And, although I never saw this in writing, people often said we were authorized one beer with lunch. That sounds like a cool Air Force, and I want to believe I was in that Air Force. But the Air Force I was in made me take a Homosexual Awareness Test.

What can be said of that? It was multiple choice and I probably passed with the minimum of 80 percent by clicking mostly C. So, as far as the Air Force is concerned, I am 80 percent homosexually aware. I don't know what that means nor do I know what they wanted to accomplish. Likely some General woke up in the middle of the night screaming because he'd realized there might actually be homosexuals in his Air Force? He was aware and that meant we all had to be aware, and the only way to enhance our awareness was a multiple choice test that everyone cheated on. Nah. There was probably a stupider reason than anything I can invent; I never went to Officer Training School.

I'm not sure what pills we took that night—probably Motrin 800s or something pointless. But the three of us drank Bud Light (a beer I hate save for when it's free) and stood around Matt's dorm room talking about his impending TDY. Laughter hovered around our conversation that night, but when I recall this, I'm forced to lock Laughter inside the room with us. Because we were all there, and the memory isn't real if one of us gets away.

I: Can't believe you're letting your troop go to the desert.

Adam: What am I supposed to do about it?

I: *(Pointing to Matt)* Break his finger or something.

Laughter nods at this suggestion and leans against the nightstand.

Matt: *(Sits on his bed, the springs creak. He swigs his beer)*

Adam: That's stupid. How will we explain it?

Laughter brings fist to chin.

I: Doesn't matter. Can't do shit after it's broke. Real world. Real consequences.

—You didn't say that.

—Those words orbited the words I did say.

Matt: *(Adjusts his gold-framed glasses)* How about a toe instead?

I: Yeah. A toe then.

Laughter shrugs, pats pockets for cigarettes.

Matt: *(Unties left boot and tugs it off, then plants his black-socked foot on the floor)*

Adam: How should I do it?

I: *(Offering Matt's G.I. chair to Adam)* Smash this on his foot.

Laughter furrows brow, pulls orange BIC from breast pocket and thumbs sparks.

Adam: This is a terrible idea.

I: But it's a great idea to let him go to the desert and die.

Laughter stands, and then walks to door.

I: He'd do it for you.

Laughter tries doorknob. Door is locked. Sits cross-legged on floor, lights cigarette and puffs vigorously to fill room with smoke.

Adam continues to say smart things and I say stupid, hurtful things, until finally Adam snatches the chair and slams the square leg on Matt's foot. The chair cracks from the impact and Matt says nothing—just finishes his beer, and then pulls his boot back on. I laugh and say, "I can't believe you just did that." Adam tosses the broken chair aside, and it collapses in a heap. We go back to work like we hadn't drank, popped pills, or smashed a chair on Matt's foot. Laughter did not follow us back to work, and I don't know what became of the chair.

*

Here's a real war story. I went to Saudi Arabia and never got shot at, never pulled nor even touched a trigger, nor did I run for the cover of a bunker when a SCUD never came flying at me because I'm not the kind of guy who runs and hides from missiles that are never fired. I did not fear for my life at any point while in the desert despite the fact that on CNN every day tanks "prepped the battlefield" or blasted inanimate objects into oblivion in their pursuit of animate objects. I fought a war in complete security—fearless because there was nothing for me to fear.

And the day that poor bastard draped an American flag over a toppled Saddam statue, I was in Saudi. Me and everyone I worked with turned our heads and tugged on our DCU butterfly collars like Rodney Dangerfield because we knew with some slight changes in circumstance, any one of us could have been the guy holding the flag.

People who say that they'd never have done it that way can kiss my ass. Pontification after the fact is wholly divorced from deciding in the moment, and that guy just chose poorly while a camera was on him. If a camera was on me all the time, people would see me in a different way too. Good or bad, I don't know or care. But they'd see me through a camera lens. And it doesn't matter how wide your flat-screen TV is, or if it's so high-def that the plasma melts your face off, there will always be things happening off-screen that matter and things that happened before the camera was turned on. Things will continue to happen once the camera's off. On-screen. Off-screen. It all matters, and no one person can see it all.

*

Matt came to work the next day with a full cast on his foot. He didn't go TDY. Someone did because someone always has to go, but I don't know who went, and because I don't know, I don't have to care.

When it was my time to go to Saudi, I went. I didn't try to get out of it or run away to Canada (which I couldn't have done legally anyway thanks to a law enacted by a bunch of bastards too old to get drafted whether a draft is reinstated or not—an age I look forward to). And I was there when Matt's foot was broken and was glad that he didn't have to go do some stupid job that I wouldn't wish on anyone.

—What about people you hate?

—Send 'em to the sandbox.

I wasn't always against the war, and I won't say that I was just because that's the popular thing to say when a war goes wrong. Wars don't go right. Fewer people might die than in other wars; that's statistically different. But once war is, it can't be reset. And the only thing that being there helped me to see clearly is that no matter what side I stand on, pointing fingers at those who stand across from me won't breathe life into any of the dead or erase the images that keep men and women awake at night—real and imagined. And being there didn't help me see anything more clearly than that no matter what side I stand on, pointing fingers at those who stand across from me won't breathe life into any of the dead or erase the images that keep men and women awake at night—real and imagined.

Before I joined, Dad told me, "Son. There's a big war about every ten years." He was right this time, and I went and came home and never went back. Other guys went and came home, or they went and didn't come home. Some went and came home, and then went back and never came home. I didn't know any of the guys who died over there and never will.

*

One day in a journalism class at WVU this man came in and showed us some stop-motion video his company was working on—another desperate attempt at news innovation. It was a map of Iraq. Stupid music played in the background; the kind that tells your brain: show everyone that you are sad now. As the song played, tiny red dots popped up on the map. Each dot, he said, represented a soldier who'd died. The man stood up front and gauged our reactions while dots filled Iraq's borders. He knew those dots would fill up the map and make people cry, that the music would instruct them how to react. And I hated him for turning dead soldiers into red dots, and I hated him for using dead soldiers to sell a product. Some people in the class cried or bit their lips, and I kept my mouth shut. I could say that I didn't want to ruin it for them, but the truth is I was afraid that saying something would hurt my grade.

I didn't stand up and tell that man I hated him that day, and I won't say I hate that man and his dot-covered map now. Because if I hate him, I must hate myself. I hope a better person with something better to say waits farther down the line, and I fear my truths will bring me nothing more than failure. But I won't fail because I said nothing. Silence kills too.

*

Halloween night of 2003 in Old Town Alexandria, months before Adam broke Matt's foot, Matt and I stumbled out of a bar after last call and searched for the parking garage where a couple friends waited on us. We headed down a side street that we agreed was the right direction. A black Nissan Spyder was parked on the street and a Saudi Arabian flag was on the dash.

"I hate spiders," I said. Because I hate arachnids—the pointy legs and fangs and venom.

We walked on, and after some time, passed the same car.

"This is the wrong way," Matt said.

"No it isn't."

"That's the same Spyder," he told me.

"I hate spiders," I said again, because I am a spider bigot.

"Wanna fuck it up?" he asked.

"You kick one side-view-mirror, and I'll kick the other one— simultaneous."

I lined up to kick the hell out of the passenger-side mirror, and we counted down from three. I ran and leapt into the air and kicked as hard as I could but hit nothing. When I landed, I crumpled on the ground and felt an intense pain in my left knee, a pain that I'd felt my senior year at football practice when my knee-cap slipped off to the side of my leg.

Matt rounded the car and said, "Dude, I missed."

"Help me up," I groaned.

He looked at me, then turned and looked up the street. We hadn't done anything, which I believe was a miracle, but I could see in his eyes that he wanted to run. I wouldn't have blamed him for leaving me in the gutter. Whatever punishment came my way for attempted stupidity was deserved, although it's difficult to punish someone for doing nothing. Instead, Matt helped me to my feet, and when he did, my knee-cap slipped back into place. Constant pain replaced the intense pulses and that consistency was something I managed with gritted teeth.

We hobbled back to the parking garage, my arm tossed around his neck. Our heavy breaths burst steam puffs into the cold air, and once we'd almost reached our destination I saw a black man in a field jacket and jeans standing on the corner of some street and another. We'd passed him earlier that evening and he'd asked for change. I didn't have any because I never carry cash. I feel better about myself when I don't have to lie to someone begging for money, so I'd told the man I was sorry I couldn't help, and then walked a couple blocks and drank myself stupid. As we passed him this time, he shouted, "That's right, boys. Never leave a man behind."

Sometimes those phrases press so hard against the back of my teeth that I can't swallow them, and I'll mutter them to myself and snort. I'm not sure how I feel about those words, but I am sure that I never saw that man on the street again, and I haven't heard from Matt in five or six years—which is fine with me. Because we don't have shit to talk about anyway.

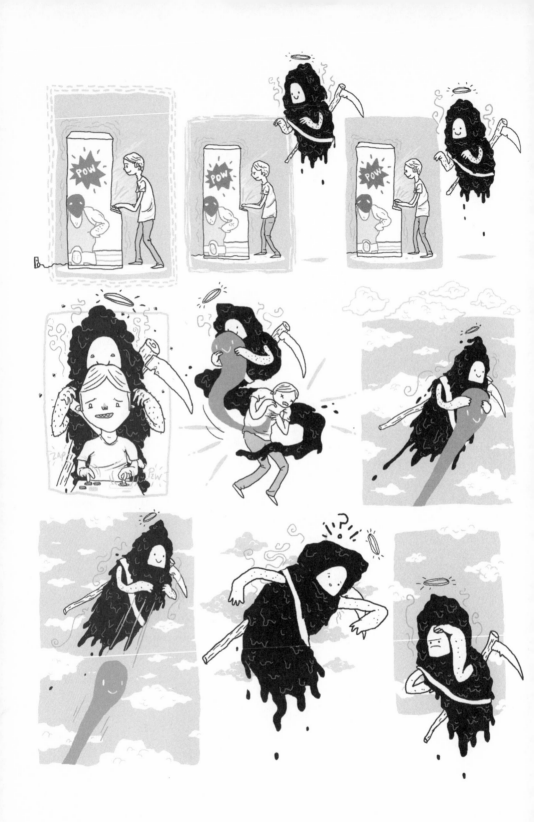

Lillian-Yvonne Bertram

I Believe the Far Fields Are Made of Glass

& research. Corn-clad & thick on moans. There at the edge of the wheel

the tar bubbles burst and they kept on bursting as long as the mile stayed

a mile which it did. What they did not want to speak of, the men burned

out there: pasture, polio rags, poplin junk as long as there was a day to

foul which was a long while. Tar a wincing mammal. Someone asked if

I missed my friends. The more erotic pints we shared. But I squeezed &

pulled one damp loaf down from the shelf after another. Donning a mania

all his own, Teddy Roosevelt believed in boar hunts and war-suckled men.

He'd have something to say about this enterprising sunset, the shivering

alfalfa, trim and sweet like champagne.

LEE MILENA GOODMAN

Barter System

V.

They both get evicted after they lose their jobs but they are young and not tied down and can suck it up. Tack, at least, can take it like a man. California is starting to feel like bad luck so they decide to go up country.

On the way out, Tack lets Hicham pick the last place they would eat in the state. They come off the freeway and park at a roadside stop with prices on a sign. Hicham asks for extra peppers, Thanks. The girl with black hair at the counter says, Okay. Tack one ups him, Do what you do to his and then do it even more to mine, and then he looks at Hicham, and back at her.

She likes Tack better. She looks at the coworker behind her and grins. Her coworker runs all the way to the back, her lips folded in her mouth like she's trying to swallow them.

Tack can't eat real easy as his share is more peppers than food. He tells Hicham he's not hungry. When Tack brings his tray back to the girl he tips her two dollars they don't have because she did what he asked.

They get back into the truck and drive to the brink of California before it gives up to Oregon. They go to a motel only because Hicham wants a shower.

For a bed, Hicham chooses the floor. But Tack's no softie. He moves to the floor. Hicham says he's not getting up. Tack says the same. Whereas Hicham grabs a sheet and some pillows, Tack doesn't need anything, and he lies there until dawn, listening to Hicham sleep.

In the morning, Tack grabs free cups of coffee downstairs at check out and brings them up to the room.

Thanks, Hicham says. He raises the cup to his mouth like a lady at high tea.

All right, Tack says, Don't start crying or anything.

They get back in the truck and head off. Tack insists on driving out to Oregon as he is no passenger. On the second night of their trip they stay in an ocean campsite near the start of Washington. The ridged bottom of the truck bed is a hard metal mattress that suits Tack's spine.

Tack wakes Hicham up the next morning by stepping on his head so he can piss outside.

You overslept, Tack says, What's wrong? Couldn't pass out last night? But Hicham says, No. Slept fine.

Is that a fact? Tack grits teeth that can grind iron. You didn't wake up, not once, not at all?

Maybe once, Hicham rubs his trampled head.

I knew it, Tack says, Truck too hard for you? He kicks sand back at the ocean. It sails up loose to the sky. He throws the keys at Hicham.

Tack lets him drive them out of Oregon because he feels so inclined. He doesn't remember when they got to Washington. He might have dozed off because he is comfortable doing so.

Well, hey, Hicham says, You fell asleep there for awhile. He smirks at Tack like this means something.

I was just thinking with my eyes closed, Tack says, I saw you look over at me to see if I was sleeping. It's not like I've always got to respond to you.

Night's coming on and they penetrate Washington. Tack takes the wheel at the next gas station because he feels like driving again. They buy peanuts salted in the shell. Hicham puts the whole thing in his mouth and spits the shell out before he gums his old lady craw on the nut. Tack, he eats the shells and spits the nut out.

Tack pushes east through to South Dakota, Home of Mount Rushmore where founding fathers were dynamited into stone, where rock was shown who's boss. Home of Deadwood. Home of the Badlands. Land of the Black Hills and inhospitable greatness. They pass by signs for Wall Drug and Tack and Hicham look at each other and have a feeling they, too, are home. Well, Tack knows he's home. He worries for Hicham sometimes, not like a momma's worry, but like a man might worry that his car's on the brink of breaking down, or that he's got to put his favorite hunting dog to sleep because she keeps biting too hard on the necks of the game.

They see a sign for Rapid City and head straight for it. Tack likes the sound of this. Rapid City. It comes up fast and tough. It waits for no one. Tack's eyes get wide as he looks around town. It almost sounds like Rabid City, and Tack dreams about this for a second.

IV.
The streets run flat, the sky is enormous, and everything is quiet; maybe too quiet, in a sneaky way. They park downtown and get out of the truck. Good afternoon, an old man teeters past them. He's got a vet's cap on. Tack's eyes follow the Vet to see where he is headed, after all, the man has made it this far.

Tack and Hicham have never had such a need for a job. They both know about waiting tables. They both know how to run a cash register, and this, especially, Tack has noted, is a skill everyone should have. America doesn't run on some barter system. They head first for the biggest building on the block into where the Vet had disappeared: the Alex Johnson Hotel. They come in to bison heads all over the walls, with giant swastikas behind them.

I'm not crying, Tack says, But there are swastikas all over the walls of this Nazi hotel.

These aren't for Nazis, Hicham says, These swastikas run the other way.

Tack doesn't take chances. He wants to fit into this place for now, later they can overthrow the Third Reich. Reverse swastikas. Like when the flag is flown upside down, something Tack would never do, but he has heard of this. Tack keeps a lookout for the Vet, and now maybe things are coming together. The Vet, a double agent who reversed the swastikas himself and no one cared to notice. It is hard to tell what way these flags run, anyhow.

Tack goes up to the lady at the front desk. He raises his hand and says, Heil. Can me and my friend have an application? She gives him a couple. He looks up and around at all the possibilities. The hotel has restaurants, a bar, souvenir shops, or he could just push her out of the chair and tie her down and do her job handing out applications all day to people. He looks over the desktop to her fat ankles to see if she'd already thought of this move herself. She hadn't. But Hicham comes up behind him and leave it to him to mess up something like this.

They turn the applications in to Soft and Lazy up at the desk. Hicham starts to walk away, but Tack knows the drill. He asks to see a manager. She says, He's busy. Tack says, We'll wait. She says, All right. He tells her, As long as it takes. And he winks at her.

Tack sits in a big leather chair and he is feeling fine about the tall ceilings and air conditioning. It smells dusty, a gunsmoked West, and he imagines outlaw fire all over the hotel lobby. Tack stares and smiles at Desk Fatty. Hicham says he's hungry and goes to the souvenir shop. He brings them back a box full of buffalo jerky. Tack looks at the bison on the walls as he chews on them all salted and shrunk down. He looks at Fatty, it might as well be you, he thinks to her, he smiles and chews some more.

The manager is down in no time; a Boss for Now who Tack can relate to as he can cut right to the chase, Bell-hop or janitor? Tack says, Bell-hop, we won't disappoint. Hicham gets pouty but Tack says he's going to love the get-up. Maybe we'll wear white gloves. Hicham says he doesn't want to carry around luggage all day. Tack asks would he rather carry around a pink feather duster?

Janitors don't have to deal with anyone directly, Hicham says.

What are you afraid of? Some bad man yelling at you?

That's not what I'm afraid of, he says.

But Tack knows it is. Hicham is a shy violet still on momma's apron strings.

The Boss for Now says the boys will share a room for a piece out of their paychecks, get fifty percent off on eating in the hotel and thirty percent off buying at the convenience shops. They can mail things here, use the hotel laundry. It is like a little city at the Alex Johnson. A little German city.

They settle in their room, eighth floor. Hicham uses the closet and Tack uses the drawers. They get set to bell-hop. They do have uniforms, and the Boss for Now would like the boys to look a little groomed. Hicham shaves off his stubble in a minute. Tack, it takes fifty minutes and two razors. They look at each other in uniform. Long slacks. Fitted jackets. Hard shoes. They get hats if they want them, and gloves (Tack knew it) for winter.

Tack practices the goose-step down the hall, every part of him gunshot straight. Hicham runs out after him when he finishes locking up the room.

Quit it, says Hicham, when he catches up to Tack. We aren't soldiering or anything.

And Tack says, Right, and clucks his tongue, and looks again for the Vet.

They are trained in no time by a teenaged kid named Jerry the Doorman who whistles for taxis. Bell-hops don't usually have to deal with getting taxis, but Jerry wants to show them everything, as surely he recognizes greatness.

Tack is strong and can handle even the biggest bags. He doesn't need a cart, even when the hotel guests insist. Little Boy Hicham always rolls the cart around. He'd skip to the elevator in those tight shoes if he could.

III.

Over the weeks they spend their tips for fun but save their checks for necessities. There are few of these. They live downtown and never have to drive anywhere; they walk to the local bars. It is hot this summer so they make mainly night trips. From one of the hotel souvenir shops, Tack buys a new knife. Hicham gets jeans that Tack promises do not make his ass look big, Sweetheart.

Hicham says, Shut up, that he didn't ask, but Tack knows he was thinking it.

It turns out Pretty Boy's buying new clothes because he's in love with Fatty downstairs.

She's not fat, Hicham slaps Tack on the back, Besides she's beautiful and has huge tits.

I know you mean teats, Tack says, Always a momma's boy looking for a feeding.

Come to find out Momma likes him back. Tack would rather stay on guard than fraternize with the enemy, anyway. Who knows who is up to what in this place. Late at night, Tack leaves the room to stand at attention by the elevator doors. He puts his ear to room eyeholes. He wears his uniform even in his time off to be ready to take them all down: Fatty, the Boss for Now, the "guests," maybe even Hicham if he gets sucked up into something. Tack hopes not but if it comes down to it.

Hicham and Tack save up enough to go eat at the hotel steak house. Hicham wants Fatty to come along. Then Hicham says maybe it should be just him and Fatty. Tack knows Hicham's embarrassed for him to see her eat, but Tack doesn't mind, so he makes Hicham feel better by going. Tack wears his uniform to dinner. His blond hair is in a high and tight. His face is smooth. Good thing he is jut-jawed and fierce and has cold gunmetal eyes. He could be prettier than Hicham, but he is more killer than charmer.

Fatty eats all her food, like Tack expects her to, and she wants dessert. Tack looks down at his white gloves that he has kept spotless all through dinner just like an officer. They wait for Bananas Foster. Tack glares over at other tables to make sure people are minding their manners. He sees the Vet who is with twelve other men and women. The Vet is dressed in white and blue and all he needs is a little red but who the hell is Tack or Hicham or anybody else to say a thing. Just by being, the Vet is more than anyone. He is infinity more than that family speaking German settling into the corner, giving orders to the naïve waitress, who, with her orange hair and buck teeth, should be giving orders to them.

A waiter drops off on-fire bananas in the middle of Tack's table. Tack reaches out to stop him from killing the juice and cutting the blaze but he's already gone and smothered it. Fatty and Hicham have at ruined banana hell. Tack gets back on point.

It is a family of four Tack is watching. Parents and a son and daughter. They are shameless about the German-speaking. The lingo is fighting its way across the room, busting up Tack's ears. He is trying to turn it into English by the time it hits his brain. He plugs up the sound with pointed white fingers so he can hear his own red red blood ring bells of liberty. He looks at Fatty and Hicham. He looks at the Vet. He looks back at the Germans.

The little German girl is in the lap of the mother. The mother is clapping the little girl's hands together. The father reaches into a green hotel bag from the souvenir shop and puts a cowboy hat on the head of his son, then shakes his son's hand fake hard. The son reaches up one finger and tilts his new hat to rest it on the back crown of his head.

Tack unplugs his ears. He looks over at Fatty wiping the evidence from her maw. She says, I could do with another. When Bucky Firehead comes to pick up the empty plate, Hicham orders for Fatty. Bucky says, One for a table isn't enough, it never is.

Tack rubs his hands together. This time, he'll make sure to let the Vet's table know that where there is smoke there is fire and he is on board. He could be a double agent himself, after all, like a termite bringing the

whole place down inside out. Tack "the Termite" Moss, better than Boll
Weevil, or maybe it could be Hicham "the Boll Weevil" Feist as well if he
catches on quick enough. Tack doubts it.

Bucky carries over a second burning plate to put in front of Fatty. Fatty
squeals happy and Bucky is about to destroy the whole thing like the other
guy so Tack reaches out and grabs the plate. It's Bucky's fault the fire
slides off and lands on the table, and on her hand a little, all of it ruined
quick by three glasses of water. As the table smokes and steams, Tack
looks over at the German family, raises one eyebrow, points at them and
then points at the table, then at Bucky. Bucky swings out with her barely
burned hand and hits Tack just right. He hears her scream at him as he
stares sideways at the floor, now on his cheek, and he mumbles, I love a
redhead.

As Tack rubs his chin he catches the Vet's eye. He gets up and walks over
to the thirteen. An old vet's lady gets out a mirrored compact and makes
with the lipstick, but Tack knows better, and wishes he remembers Morse.

Heil, he says, in the know. Reverse swastikas, this place will be
overrun in no time for sure.

The Vet gives Tack a big wide, Hi.

Heil, Tack clacks his feet together. An old vet's lady closes her
mirrored compact as the Vet's mouth falls open.

Tack whispers loud across the rectangle table, As in Hitler? and juts a
thumb back over his shoulder at the Germans.

Tack is kicked to the ground by four of the old vets and one old vet's lady.
Tack is laughing, Thank you sir may I have another. Ja, he screams, they
give him another. JA. He then says, Nein NEIN. They kick him harder.
The German woman walks over screaming an English stop. It is only
now that Tack screams the American uncle, as he realizes that this is no
initiation.

By the end, the vets are no longer allowed in the Alex Johnson. The
German momma speaking broken never-to-be-fixed English to the
management about double-locking doors and windows and fear for life in

U S of A, is compensated with free tickets to Mount Rushmore and maybe she will change her mind when she sees the enormous forefathers looking past her with truly benevolent indifference.

When Tack comes to on a couch in the hotel lobby, he is told by the restaurant manager that he will have to be fired for, whatever he has done, he has done it in uniform. The Boss for Now is working late and comes down from the office to explain this himself. He does it by the concierge desk alongside of Hicham and Fatty, who tell Tack what an idiot he is in front of Boss for Now, so Tack tells Hicham to go and suck on Momma's teat, and the Boss for Now says he does not approve of affairs in the workplace, and fires Hicham and Fatty, too. Tack gets up to slap his knees he is laughing so hard. Fatty sits down to cry because now how is she going to feed herself. Hicham screams at him, his voice high, his cheeks red. Tack tells him he's pretty when he's angry and Hicham strides off, leaving Tack and Fatty down there in the hotel lobby.

Tack looks at Fatty, he tells her even though he thinks she's Fat he agrees with his friend that she has great tits. He also tells her that she can do better. He goes and sits next to her on the long lobby couch. She stops crying, says he's right, and leaves through the revolving door. She pushes it so hard it swirls a few times after she goes, the breeze hitting his shiners. Then the door stops and his eyes heat up again. It is a good burn. He goes upstairs and tells Hicham she up and left and not to worry. That he can do better. Hicham shoves him hard and Tack sleeps on the floor.

The next morning they get a wake-up call for a checkout time of high noon or else the Boss for Now will kick their asses. Rapid City is starting to feel like bad luck so they take to driving again. Hicham asks for Tack to drop him off somewhere, he is tired and embarrassed. Tack says, Don't be silly, I won't tell anyone about Fatty. Tack punches him in the arm and Hicham doesn't move.

II.
They get out of the sun's way and head for Wall Drug, Free Ice Water. There must be a billion cash registers they can punch numbers into at

this myth of a drug store. They left their last checks behind at the Alex Johnson. While Hicham was packing their room, Tack told New and Ugly at the desk he and his friend didn't need their money.

Tack and Hicham hit Wall early on into morning, pulling off of pavement, driving onto dust, pulling back onto Cheyenne river rock. They do not notice the particulars aside from a four-year-old girl at the main entrance. She is running around with her shirt off, happy and free, before someone tells her she can't anymore.

They don't chase after the girl, but they do tug at the doors and wonder from where she came. Wall Drug is a ghost town at this time in the morning. The directory talks it up about clothing and book and souvenir stores, but these are locked. What is not behind bars and windows is a giant main street backyard, where inscriptions invite picture-taking for memories. A general store is all that stands in the way between them and a bucking bronco, stuffed, never to be ass over tea kettle. Look at me long and good, Tack's hand is on the horse's rump, Remember this. Tell it back to me later.

A scent of food rounds them up to a cracked back entrance of the saloon towards a kitchen. They stop at the dark wood diner countertop. On the other side a woman with triple-pierced ears says, You're early, but what can I do you for? Tack says, Can me and my friend have an application? Hicham eyes the chalkboard menu, then grabs a plastic one from between a mustard-and-ketchup bottle set.

All right, she goes to the register and tears a couple off a pad of paper, I don't know if we are hiring but we are always accepting applications. Tack smiles at Hicham. Oh, they'll be hiring us all right, Tack says under his breath. They can't afford not to. They fill out the sheets and Tack asks to see the manager.

I am the manager, the woman says.

Oh, Tack holds out his hand to shake hers, Well, then, he says. He points to the applications, What do you think? The right stuff, I know.

She taps one bandaged nail against the countertop, Sure, sure. She looks over the sheets. Like I said, she starts, We always accept applications, but I don't know if we are hiring.

Tack says nothing back.

Well, she takes out a pencil, What can I get you gentlemen to eat?

Hicham scratches his nose and starts to say but Tack tells her, I don't know if we are ordering.

Hicham says, Tack, I'm ordering, and Tack takes Hicham's menu, putting it under his dry armpit.

Hicham looks back at the chalkboard.

Tack gets ready to cobra spit and knock the sign down but the woman, who has already left and come back, brings them two glasses of Free Ice Water. Just like on the billboards, she says. He had seen it, but it never registered. Wall Drug, Free Ice Water…he's onto them. Free Water? Wall Drug, Free Gas Garbage and Electric? And to top it off she adds, Tell you what, you two look like you need a little pick-me-up. How's about some normally a nickel-a-cup coffee, on-the-house?

With cream and sugar please, says Hicham, like he was expecting this, his brown eyes look over trying to but can't quite pierce Tack's gray. Brown's too soft.

Tack puts down the menu.

The woman goes to grab a pot. She turns the cups in front of them over to fill with coffee, and gives Hicham cream and sugar packets.

Sera, she yells, Come here so I can mind you, and scoots off to the kitchen. The topless girl has black hair like her momma. She pulls a chair out, hoists herself up, sits next to Hicham and stares. Hicham takes his shirt off and stares back, and smiles and elbows Tack who does the same.

A quiet child. They can't even hear her breathe loud kid breath but they can see her lungs fill up. She runs behind the counter to tear off an application, grabs a pen, and draws three successive underlines to play hangman.

Hicham bites. S.

Nope, she says, and draws a circlehead.

Tack says, T for Tack.

Noooo. Shaky stick body.

They look at their head and body on the paper there and rapid fire to shoot their way out of this one.

R, arm. L, arm. N, linehand. E, linehand. A, leg.

What, no goddamn fingers?

Thas no question. NutherLeg.

Hicham rubs his head hard, I.

Dangerous foot.

All right all right, Tack gets up to pace, Let me guess the next, you idiot.

Tack stops and looks into the little girl's eyes, O, O.

O, he says again.

Maybe she will change the word in her head, or, has already changed the word, or, maybe the word doesn't exist. But O marks the spot, right in the center of three spaces and lays goldenegged on top of the line.

P, Tack blurts out alphabetic.

Last foot. Dead.

Surry, the little girl draws a big frown on the dead man's face, a home-driven point.

Well, Tack watches till the frown's complete, What is it then?

Not telling, she says, but nicely she is drawing them angel wings and a halo.

Hicham nods his head, Fair enough. We don't care anyway.

She smiles at the paper and gives them devil horns and a tail.

Hicham reaches out for the paper, scowling. Tack does not mind this world before or after, but he minds a few things in it now. He pokes Hicham hard in the ribs and admits about the checks at the Alex Johnson and how, goddamn it, we need to pull a turn around. Besides, Tack goes on, as Hicham grabs his side, they shouldn't stay here anyway, making applications at the moccasins or western clothing or Black Hills Gold stores in the adjoining mall. Wall Drug is all divvied up now, and they are looking for something entire. Tack reaches over the counter, grabs back their applications from on top of the register, and makes paper cranes and airplanes for the wooden jetway all lined up and ready for takeoff.

Tack and Hicham give the little girl their shirts for when she gets big but tell her to keep running around half-naked as long as she can. Hell, all naked, until people tell her she can't. Hell, they change their minds, don't listen to anyone unless it is what you want to hear. As a matter of fact, hell, give us our shirts back. But she runs away with their tops to behind the swinging kitchen doors, and the shirtless drive back to the Alex Johnson is a fine one.

Good thing she kept the shirts, Tack says, She's going to be a woman after all one day, no one can stop that. Hicham, driving, nods Yes. Tack rubs his jaw, I'm growing my beard back, and puts bare feet out the window.

I.
They walk back into the Alex Johnson with jackets over their bare chests. Tack manages hard noises all the way up to the front desk even without spurs on the back of his high tops. He does not look for the Ex-Boss, but does look for and sees New and Ugly, shuffling papers around the desk counter. Tack looks around for New Himself-and-Hicham running around in old uniforms. Far easier to replace Fatty.

Good afternoon, Tack nods. You know what I'm back for. Tack leans in a little close, Give it here.

Ugly delays, but gets out their checks. We thought you might come back, he says, We kept them as close to the exit as possible. He tosses them at Tack's feet.

Tack takes off his jacket, he slaps Hicham's arm for him to do the same. They take off their shoes and march around until Jerry the Doorman has to ask them to please leave, he needs the job, please, please. Tack drops his shoes and jacket to start a goose-step out the door, and salutes Jerry, leaving him the clothes for when he grows up big and strong one day. As he leaves, Hicham scoops up the checks and shakes Jerry's left hand. Jerry's right is busy saluting Tack, his doorman's shrill whistle measures out the straight one-two until a smile pulls the pucker right off his face.

KATHLEEN ROONEY

We Are Bachelorettes

Look out—we are a batch of bachelorettes! The equivalent term to "bachelor" used to be "spinster," but look here, Mister, we are bachelorettes. We are the bachelorette party of our dear friend Avni, who is over thirty and about to marry. We went to high school / went to college / went to med school with Avni.

What brings us to the Knickerbocker Hotel is The Dinner Detective, an interactive murder mystery, which we totally solved! We come from right here in the city of Chicago / we come from the western suburbs / we come from central Indiana, and we bachelorettes possess a hand-written list. The list has been printed by the Maid of Honor on cream-colored card-stock. The card-stock has been handed out to teams, teams consisting of bachelorettes. We bachelorettes are sober / are tipsy / are shit-faced, but we have to find some keepsakes / some items / some shit. We bachelorettes are on a scavenger hunt, and Mister Knickerbocker Concierge, we require your

~~Hotel pen~~

Yes! Yes! We got the hotel pen. We can use it to cross off the other items on our list! We are type A people and super competitive / we are just happy to be out and away from the baby, walking around on a sultry July night in a tiny dress / we don't really care and hate games like this.

Come on, let's cut across Walton to the Drake Hotel, where they have breath-taking floral arrangements in the middle of the foyer! We are not terribly smooth criminals, so we ask the concierge there if we can maybe just take one of those yellow daisies from the mountainous planter in the lobby. She blinks behind her glasses and tells us in a Russian accent, "I can't be upset by what I can't see, you know what I mean?" And we do, we so do. We cross

~~Flower~~

off our list. We almost want to ask her if she knows that one of the meanings associated with daisies like the one we've yanked is "Innocence / I'll Never Tell." But this doesn't advance the game, so instead we say:

"Where do you think we should go next on our hunt?" and she says River North, so that's where we go.

River North's nickname is "the Viagra Triangle." We come here sometimes to try to meet affluent older men / we've never been here before tonight and are sort of impressed by the hypotenuse that is Rush Street / we used to hang out here, but thank God that nightmare's over.

We are trying to remain vigilant instead of thinking about all this, when there! In the window! A pair of insane stilettos, arranged to look loungey and regal, almost in the posture of a pair of lions, post-antelope-feast on some nature show: they are that louche, and that savage. We snap their photograph and cross

~~Picture of outrageous shoes~~

off the cream-colored card-stock, although if we are honest with ourselves, we could probably do better. Like maybe—these are Hermès, after all, and very if-you-have-to-ask-what-they-cost-then-you-can't-afford-them—these are not so much "outrageous" as they are "obscene." We resolve to keep looking.

We swing our eyes like searchlights from one side of the street to the next—scanning, scanning. In the UK we'd be "hens," in Canada "stagettes," but this is America and here? We are bachelorettes!

Check out that guy sitting on the patio at Tavern on Rush! He looks European. Look at that ponytail! And he waxes his chest. Under the table, we suspect, his shoes must be outrageous. We squeeze gracefully / squeeze awkwardly / squeeze reluctantly between the crowded tables, the better to talk to him. He kisses our hands and says "but of course," we are welcome to gaze upon his shoes. But his shoes are bland. We take a picture anyway to humor him, and his girlfriend gives us her

~~Business card~~

so hooray / fuck yeah / great, we guess, this wasn't totally pointless. We also grabbed a paper napkin, because what the hey, it was there, and we use it to fashion a

~~Makeshift wedding ring~~

much bigger than / much smaller than / much more existent than the one on our own ring finger, not that we're concerned with that type of comparison.

The repurposed trash makes us think how the word "scavenge" comes from the Middle English *scawageour,* meaning "person hired to remove refuse from the streets." Even when drinking, we are obsessed with etymology. But refuse removal is not really what we are doing! We are bachelorettes, and the term "scavenger hunt" dates from the 1940s, and what we are doing is fun and mysterious / is tolerable / is obnoxious, this being pulled arbitrarily into the orbit of attractive / of skeevy / of forgettable strangers.

And that stranger smokes! Oh my God, practically nobody still smokes. Let's ask him if he happens to have a

~~Matchbox~~

in his pocket. What luck! He does! What a sleek and classy rectangular box, and what elegant matches. They almost make us want to set something on fire, but no time for that. Where to next? North, we say, North to Division Street, whose poetic name evokes the very social ritual we are presently embarked on, the division of a girl's single life from her adult-and-actualized married-woman one / evokes anxiety about separation and aging and how these parties are really celebrations of growing further apart / evokes nothing and goes completely unremarked upon by us.

Bootleggers! Okay! Let's give that bar a try. We came here for our own bachelorette party / wouldn't normally be caught dead in a place like this / didn't know this kind of bar even existed outside of New Orleans. Two tan girls with fake tits wearing Cubs-themed bikini tops stand beside washtubs of ice and offer us beers as we walk in. No thanks, ladies—we are bachelorettes, and we are drinking only the serious stuff tonight. We cross the laser-lit dance floor, empty and air-conditioned, to the bar in the back. We belly on up.

The special is cucumber-infused vodka, the bartender tells us, which she highly recommends. The plan is to get the shots and retreat to a corner table to drink them, and then abscond with one of the shot glasses, but crap: what's this? She's poured it in like, juice glasses? What to do now? These cost $8 each! We don't want to have to do this again. The bartender is capping the bottle; she is turning her back.

We are doctors / are lawyers / are college professors, and we can't get caught stealing, but ooh dang, did you see how we lifted that

~~Shot glass~~

from the row along the edge when the bartender stopped looking for twenty seconds? And oh my God, we also grabbed a

~~Drinking straw~~

which means we are unstoppable. The other teams of bachelorettes better watch their spaghetti-strapped backs.

We are standing to leave, the post-theft endorphins rushing straight to our heads, when these two guys dash in and come over to us. They ask if we like the Cardinals, and we say hell no, this is Chicago and we love the Cubs / we say nothing because we don't even know where the Cardinals are from / we bite our tongues to keep from blurting out that sports are stupid.

"Damn right! Cubbies!" the boys say, and high-five each other.

They are so insouciant! They are just the precise, right amount of drunk! They have come to try their hand at hitting on us. These boys are so young, too young for us. These boys must be in college! Can't they see that we are thirty-one? We wonder how much longer we have until boys like them stop even noticing us / we wonder why it matters to us how old they are / we wonder at how in the past we would have felt intimidated by boys like these, but how now we feel only a sense of perfect control.

"What's with the beads?" they ask, because we are decked out. We are bachelorettes!

We tell them about our very important scavenger hunt.

"Can we help?" they ask.

We are about to say, "No, we're heading on our way," but instead it occurs to us to go, "Actually, we need a picture of a dude with his shirt off!"

They fall over each other like puppies to be that dude.

"Okay," says one, glancing down at his young and trim but not especially buff chest. "No judgment now. It's a work in progress."

And his insecurity makes us feel touched / feel mean / feel nothing really at all. After they get dressed again they insist on cheek-kisses, which we give them, because why the hell not? We are bachelorettes! Then we ask them for a

~~Mint~~

because that really is on the list, and they hand us a Tic Tac and say "Good luck, ladies!"

But we are not ladies—we are bachelorettes! And the vodka has helped us, fortified our brains! We are back on the street! The Street of Divisions!

According to Emily Post's *Wedding Etiquette,* "Whatever entertainment is planned, it should not embarrass, humiliate, or endanger the honoree or any of the guests," but fuck that: we are going to run now—in our heels, against traffic—across Division Street because we have to get a

~~Picture with another bachelorette~~

And yeah, we got honked at, but what do we care? Because we got it! On our iPhone / our digital camera / our ancient cell! We are standing outside a bar, beneath some scaffolding, in our respective fineries. Our thin / our tan / our chubby arms are around her shoulders, and she is smiling, and we are too / we are thumbs-upping / we are rolling our eyes. There is nothing like the camaraderie of bachelorettes!

We are also supposed to get a

~~Celeb photo~~

but how are we supposed to get access to any real celebs? Our jocular / resourceful / pathetic snapshot of ourselves with a Michael Jordan standee will be declared both "Hilarious" and "Disqualified" by the Maid of Honor, that fair referee / that capricious judge / that bitch.

But damn—we just looked at our phones and we are running out of time. We have to hurry up and find

~~A billboard that can also be taken as marriage advice~~

That bar! Look there! The name of it is "Chill," and even though it's not a billboard, who could deny its wisdom? We have two kids, so we know that sometimes all you can do is stay calm / we are married and realize that it's best, sometimes, not to get all worked up / we understand that desperation comes on strong—it practically has a smell—so it's best to be cool when we're on our next eHarmony date.

South! We are bachelorettes, and we have to go that way if we want to get the last two items and make it to the rendezvous point. Back down

Rush Street, on the west side this time, a buzzcut man in a pink Oxford shirt outside a bar whose walls become open windows in the summertime reaches out and grabs our wrist—playfully, we think / we hope / we doubt—and says, "How much for the beads?"

We smile at his joke / smile in relief / can't really smile.

"Girls," he says, "if you want to win your game, then you have to meet Duke."

He pauses meaningfully and cocks his head toward the inside of the bar.

And because this is exciting / this is probably the only way to win / this is how social coercion works, we let him lead us in, get the bouncer to waive the cover, and send us up the stairs to the bar Duke tends.

And just as we thought / just as we'd wanted him to be / just because sometimes the odds are defied, Duke is a) really hot and b) really nice. He agrees to help us—after all, we are bachelorettes!—find the penultimate object: a phallic item.

Duke is wracking his brain and ransacking his bar for a suitably penile piece of hardware, when we see yet another bachelorette party walk in and arrange itself at a table. We race to the bachelorettes' side as they settle themselves and—because cock is de rigueur among bachelorette parties—we say, "Hello, and by chance, do you have any phallic items?"

And as Duke comes over, about to give us a pourer from a vodka bottle, the tiara-clad bride-to-be answers, "Yes!"

She opens her clutch and hands us a hot-pink penis straw.

Duke sees he's been out-cocked and says, "Good luck, bachelorettes! Good luck with everything!"

Freud says that all a woman needs to be happy is a penis and a baby. So even those of us who don't have kids are now halfway there!

Quick now. Run! The time is almost up. We have to meet Avni the Bride and everybody else by 10:30 at Hub 51! Because once we are there, it will be clear that:

We won! We won!

What did we win? Glory, obviously. And…penis-shaped candy.

As the Maid of Honor hands us the package of rainbow-colored dicks, we think oh goody! / we think how typical / we think how silly and potentially disgusting. We will eat it right now, as though it's delicious / we will pretend to fellate it and get a cheap laugh / we will take it to work on Monday and put it in the candy jar in the office and see if anybody notices.

Come on, somebody. Somebody notice. We are bachelorettes.

Leon Baham

Earthling

Threw a prince

blanket over my

faces—not so

much a weakling—

Took me to the

canyon where

I had wrocks

in my mouth

and was not

a sissy la la—

Called me a

dirt digger—

Called me a

outside dog—

How do you say—

I'm from here

Blair Bourassa

Love is Such an Old-fashioned Word

"The limits of my language are the limits of my world."
  -Ludwig Wittgenstein

When Felix Bronislav met Helen Ferapont in 1937, she was already an expert in Panini's sutras on Sanskrit grammar. She was working on her dissertation under Nikolai Trubetzkoy in Prague, and her PhD thesis was to be a discussion of the deification of speech found in Hindu Scripture.

Felix was writing his own dissertation on the behavioralist implications of Leonard Bloomfield's analyses of the Algonquin language family. He had recently arrived from Chicago to attend a seminar by Roman Jakobson critiquing the dogmas of contemporary neogrammarian theory.

Helen was a twenty-six-year-old Bavarian of Scandinavian extraction who knew German, Norwegian, Czech, Sanskrit and French. Felix was a twenty-five-year-old Mexican Jew with Slavic roots who spoke Spanish, Portuguese, Russian, Hebrew, Cree and English.

They had very little in common.

Dr. Jakobson's seminar was masterfully delivered, and after it was over, the lecturer granted a private question and answer session to the two eager students. Helen spoke in Czech, while Felix posed his queries in a wobbly version of the doctor's native Russian. The amiable professor translated back and forth between them, and was impressed by the knowledge they both possessed of their respective fields.

When the questions of the two bright-eyed language enthusiasts had finally run dry, he invited them both to a faculty party that was to be held that night. Everyone knew that the famous soirées of the Prague Linguistic Circle were not to be missed, so both students readily accepted the offer.

*

That night they were treated to a grand spectacle, as Dr. Trubetzkoy got thoroughly poleaxed and stood up on a chair in the middle of the bar, giving his best spit-flinging imitation of Hitler (*"Wir wollen nur ein bisschen Lebensraum im Osten!"*), gesticulations and all, while literary critic Jan Mukarovský walked circles around him, reverently pistoning a fascist salute with one hand and wrapping the venerable old scholar in a roll of toilet paper with the other. Then Dr. Jakobson tottered up with his pipe and ceremoniously lit the paper on fire, igniting the old linguist like a phoenix and sending him screaming into the loo. After a few laughter-filled minutes, the legendary developer of morphophonemics emerged vengefully from the toilet with a garden hose he had somehow found in the bathroom closet and started blasting away at everyone in the place. Two men playing chess in a corner of the room soon had their board washed away by a high pressure jet of water, and were then themselves plastered against the wall and soaked to the skin. Jan charged wet-bearded into the fray with two spritzer bottles he had swiped from behind the bar and started shooting back, dousing everyone within range with a furious mixture of seltzer and Czech invective.

Felix covered Helen with his jacket while they ran laughing out of the bar, provokingly wet and exceedingly drunk. Neither one wanted to go home alone, so they headed into a nearby café. In the course of the evening they had discovered that although they had no common spoken language, they both knew enough Classical Latin and Koine Greek to be able to communicate with a blunt pencil and soggy pad of paper.

Helen laboriously explained her research, discussing in permitted detail how the word *vak* ("speech") was deified in the oldest extant Sanskrit texts, and briefly summarized Max Mueller's intriguing investigation of how the ancient Hindus had even acknowledged the interrogative particle, *ka,* as a god.

Felix was fascinated (by her voluptuous Teutonic body), and did not miss the opportunity to mention the esoteric Kabbalistic doctrine that the letters of the Hebrew alphabet are the building blocks from which the world is created, and how the text of the "Sefer Yetzirah" treats the

Jewish script as if it were a kind of periodic table. Properly arranged and joined, he explained, the letters could theoretically be used to construct living beings or even whole universes. He wrote down some examples to illustrate the point: chapter one, verse one of the King James version of the Gospel of John: *"In the beginning was the Word, and the Word was with God, and the Word was God,"* and the original Hebrew of *Psalms 33:6*:

בִּדְבַר יְהֹוָה, שָׁמַיִם נַעֲשׂוּ;   וּבְרוּחַ פִּיו, כָּל-צְבָאָם.

Helen hurriedly finished her coffee and invited him to her apartment.

He sat her down on a couch and discussed Plato's *Cratylus,* tracing Greek letters on her bare knees with a lascivious finger. But when his hand drifted more than halfway up her thigh to spell the sinuous eleventh letter of the name Aristophanes, she protested with unmistakable feminine gestures that she was not that kind of girl.

So he wrote on the pad to ask her if she ever considered the fact that the Latin alphabet comes from a code used to permit the traffic of Mediterranean contraband by the Phoenicians. Therefore they were already conversing in what was effectively a criminals' cant, and any pretentions of saintliness were inappropriate.

The sun was rising and the logic was infallible.

When they had finished, she complemented him on his performance in Latin: *"Felix,"* she said, glowing, *"bene futuis!"*

"Nam fuit ante Helenam cunnus," he panted back, *"taeterrima belli causa!"*

*

Felix delayed his return to the States and stayed with Helen, studying her German while she studied his English, as the Wehrmacht tanks rolled into the city and the jackboots began to march incessantly outside their window. In time, as the war loomed larger and more inevitable every day, they started to argue over politics.

Finally, after a horrible screaming match in half a dozen dead and tortured tongues, they separated. A week later Helen received a note in her mailbox that read:

Your beauty is like the door of a gibbering madhouse

Your beauty is like a rabid dog eyeing an infant in its cradle

Your beauty is like a whole nation of pathological anger

Your beauty is like a desert of vengeful spiny monsters living in blackened holes

Your beauty is like the hysterical ghost of a screaming homicide

Your beauty is a soul devouring opposition to paradise

Because you are no longer mine

She used the letterhead to track down his hotel and, after verifying which room was his, passed her own note under his door:

black Caribbean midnight	luscious
impossible dreams	new technology
labyrinthine psychosis	skies of fire
myself in his madness	to interest him
	sputter my redundancies
but he is a sweet	skin and eyes like some
archipelago of	to burn innocents in
a glorious and	I know nothing
would that I could lose	hardly a voice to

That night all arguments were forgotten in a rapture of sweat-soaked reconciliation. The *Realpolitik* of their relationship had become indisputable.

Felix decided to study a semester under Dr. Jakobson and postpone his thesis. Helen finished her paper on Hindu language deification and started wearing more revealing clothing. Meanwhile the telegraph wires burned with scalding floods of information. Stalin purged. Fascists took Spain. Kristallnacht raged in Berlin.

Then in June of 1938, Dr. Trubetzkoy, mentor and inspiration to both, was arrested for being an opposition sympathizer and died of a heart attack while under Nazi interrogation. The Prague Institute almost immediately fell apart, and Helen's last tenuous allegiance to the Reich finally died. They decided it was time to leave, so they took a train to Lisbon just before Germany invaded Poland.

*

In the four weeks it took to cross the Atlantic, as a way of forgetting the friendships and chaos that they were leaving behind, they discussed the works of Ferdinand de Saussure, and how he had determined that the relationship between the form of a word and the thing it signifies is completely arbitrary. They experimented with this idea, and by the time they had arrived in the US, they had created a whole new vocabulary understandable only to themselves. For example, the word *bed* became "railroad," *candle* became "Jesus," massage became "Alexanderplatz," *kiss* became "leopard skin," and *loneliness* was symbolized by the number "27."

America when they arrived seemed like a blessed island of peace in a world on fire. They moved into a flat together and reinitiated their linguistic pursuits at the University of Chicago, soon becoming professors of Structural Linguistics and Modern Languages.

Meanwhile the League of Nations collapsed. Trotsky was assassinated in Mexico. Bombs rained on London. One and a half million people died at Stalingrad.

*

Eventually their love life came to revolve around code-breaking. "Ake-may ove-lay u-tay e-may..." she would whisper to him in a crowded room in Pig-Latin. At university parties, as everyone sat around discussing the theories of Von Neumann, McLuhan, Derrida, Greenberg, and Lacan, he would be tapping out Morse code on her knee, expressing his deepest desires...

".. / .-.. . .-.. .-.. .-.. .-.. / .-. . . .-.. / .- / .... .-.. .-- .-- .-- .-- .... "

After the war finally ended, Alfred Korzybski's intriguing theory came out that human beings' knowledge is limited by the structure of their languages and nervous systems, and Bill Burroughs began hypothesizing that language was actually a biological virus specifically designed to restrict our ability to understand the world. Around the same time, a new literary genre was being born, and a plethora of artificial languages were being manufactured by its authors: Anthony Burgess' *A Clockwork Orange* was written in Nadsat, Frank Herbert's *Dune* characters conversed in Chakobsa, and J.R.R. Tolkien's elves spoke Sindarin. Meanwhile, Dr. James Cooke Brown claimed to have created the "perfect language," Loglan, and Lázaro Zamenhof was trying to proselytize the planet to the possible world peace benefits of his Esperanto.

So Helen and Felix, who by now were both well-established professors and working together at Cambridge, decided that they would try to develop their own ideal language, made up of the most appropriate words chosen from various languages around the world to more fully express their emotions. A tossed salad of Spanish, French, Portuguese and Italian vocabulary was determined to be the most appropriate for romantic interludes, while apologetic and humble formulations were absorbed from East Asia, confidence and certainty expressions were taken from a Southern States dialect of American English, and swear words were borrowed from the West Germanic branch of the Indo-European language family. After a few weeks of experimentation, they soon found they preferred Côte-d'Azur French when they made love, and Berliner *Hochdeutsch* when they argued.

They also decided to create their own special terminology to express certain complicated concepts, like *majimb,* "the feeling of insecurity that arises when around someone much more attractive (or charismatic) than oneself," *kwillol,* "the moment when you realize what you should have said or done moments before," and *shlaklez,* "the electric shiver specific to Helen when a certain area of her neck was touched." They also developed a lexicon for subtle semantic differences otherwise incommunicable, like *tyawol,* "the apathetic sense that is equated with pessimism," and *djileen,* "the apathetic sense that is equated with realism."

Over time, *djileen* became one of the most ubiquitous words used in the couple's daily conversation, as they witnessed the bloody birth of

Israel, the creation of the hydrogen bomb, and the death of a million and a half people in Korea.

*

They did their best to try to forget the horrors of the world around them, and immersed themselves in books and study. Poetry had always been the couple's shared passion, and when Noam Chomsky published his revolutionary *Syntactic Structures* in 1957, in which he developed the idea that the applications of human languages are distinct from those of mechanized computer languages due to the potentially infinite use of finite means, the two lovers never tired of passing each other bizarre love letters to test the limits of infinity.

Helen went through a phase where she ran all her words together, and eliminated all punctuation, leaving Felix poems like…

"Ivmasacrdendlesmidnitesinyrname,
Shadrdictionariesonthhardnssofyrbody…"

And he would write her back in boustrophedon…

"I watch her like
dlrow eht fo dne eht ot denrut noisivelet a
I want her like
taeh elgnuj a ni etanargemop a
I hear her like
"…sdrow fo gninaem eht gnirevocsid dlihc a

Then Lyndon Johnson and the Vietnam War made their appearance, like a murder of giant crows suddenly crashing through the couple's bedroom window, and their enthusiasm for poetry quickly faded. The evil Viet Cong and the horrific dictator Ho Chi Minh skewered babies on bayonets, while the glorious American defenders of freedom charged gallantly to the rescue of a beleaguered and thankful Indochina.

As the conflict progressed, Felix and Helen became fascinated with the recently posited Sapir-Whorf hypothesis of linguistic determinism. Examples of the phenomenon were being cited by researchers all around the world. The Hopi Indians had no word (or concept) for "past" or "future!" An obscure nation of New Guinea had only two colours in their language and its people were similarly physiologically limited! The Inuit used seven different words for "snow!"

Books began extrapolating the political consequences. In the Newspeak of George Orwell's *1984,* the semantic concept of freedom had been eliminated. In Ayn Rand's *Anthem,* a collectivist dystopia banned the use of the first person singular, and Aldous Huxley's *Brave New World* had cultivated a whole nation of people who could speak only in slogans.

Felix watched the *collateral damage, pacification,* and *enhanced interrogation technique* cluttered evening news as he reread Orwell's hypothesis that if humans could not form the words to express the ideas underlying "revolution," then they could never be able to revolt. Helen sat with Kelemperer's *Notebook of a Philologist* on her lap, considering how the Nazis had converted the minds of the German people to National-Socialism by the creation of ingenious neologisms like *Sonderbehandlung* ("special treatment," i.e. "murder") and *Volksgemeinschaft* ("people's society," i.e. "the Aryan race"). Both started to develop an eerie dread of media-customized language being used as a weapon of war.

So they decided to do their part for world peace and banned words like *war, hate, enemy, us,* and *them* from their daily vocabulary, replacing them with "lunacy," "fear," "misunderstood acquaintance," and "we."

But the wars never stopped and the hate raged on. Millions were massacred in Bangladesh. The Cultural Revolution plunged China into a decade of madness. The Ayatollah arose in Iran.

*

They passed their middle age travelling and conducting field work, often separating for months at a time to pursue diverging interests, as they researched obscure and dying languages in dusty corners of demographic maps.

Helen went to revolutionary China to study both Mandarin and the praying-mantis school of tai chi in Shandong province, writing verbose and melancholy letters back to Felix, ending each epistle with luxurious postscripts in a calligraphy that dripped libidinously off the page:

举头望明月
低头思故乡

Felix returned from working with the Bedouin and taught Helen how to communicate by glottal clicks without opening her mouth, and they spent weeks without saying a word around the house.

Meanwhile, Helen's study of Japanese dialects used by American immigrants had led her to suggest the addition of polysemous verbs to their personal vocabulary. Felix was game, and the verbs *tsuku* and *kakeru* were soon being tossed around copiously by both. *Tsuku* in Japanese can mean "to stick to," "to have," "to attend," "to follow," "to side with," "to cost," "to hold (a position)," "to push," "to be possessed (by a demon)," "to thrust," "to tilt," "to toll (as a bell)," "to come on (as a light)," "to burn," "to enter (a profession)," "to arrive," "to husk," "to attach," and "to be obsessed," depending on the context it is in. Similarly, *kakeru* has the meanings "to lack, ""to chip," "to wane (the moon)," "to hang," "to trap," "to cover," "to squirt/water," "to span/bridge," "to lock," "to button," "to offer," "to encourage," "to spend (time)," "to brake," "to play (music)," "to start (an engine)," "to call (by phone)," "to bring," "to submit," "to multiply," "to insure (a house)," "to pressure (someone)," "to suspect," "to finish," "to iron," "to brush," "to screen (applicants)," " to be concerned about," "to tax," "to perch," "to wish (on a star)," "to rest," "to wear," "to run," and "to bet."

Vocabulary was thereby greatly reduced, but it soon got monotonous saying the same words so often, and they decided to leave polysemes to the Japanese. The planet continued to burn around them as they rearranged their personal lexicon one more time. Millions starved in Ethiopia. AIDS appeared. Chernobyl exploded.

*

The world, however, continued to turn. Years passed and gently pushed the aged linguists into rocking chairs. Clocks spun and calendars were hung up and replaced. Years and decades went by. Their car rusted and old friends died. Fashions and presidents changed. Finally, in 1988, after fifty years together, Felix was diagnosed with terminal lung cancer.

After three years, he was placed in palliative care to await his final passing. For a month, Helen never left his side, holding his hand, brushing her fingers through his hair, smiling into his eyes.

They both realized then that after all their little codes and games, their foreplays and teases, they had finally succeeded in achieving their ultimate goal. They had created the perfect language, absolutely minimalist and consummately expressive, consisting of only a single word—which never need be spoken.

JP GRITTON

Windrows

In September, Mitt will turn eighteen, but it is now, in the long, hot weeks and months of summer, that something kicks the machine into being. In the sweltering hours at Jack Crider's farm, he thinks he can see this thing moving, thinks he can make out its shape in the groaning black mouth of the hay baler, in the whir of struts and tine, in a dark cloud over a black river, in bare trees swinging in the wind. It's coming for him—still more or less shapeless now, still nothing but dark clouds and naked trees— but the edges are getting sharper. A tornado comes through Mountain View and tears a man in half; a little boy drowns in the Jacks Fork; Lester McCullers' daughter has a baby that people say is Lester McCullers'. And Vietnam is on television: trees and trees and rivers like bacon drippings, GIs smiling but sunk-eyed and muddy. In their eyes is that same reckless, stillborn look of moonshiners who have drunk themselves blind.

"Korea weren't pretty," says William, his father, one afternoon, "but I believe this one's even uglier."

Summer's stillness accumulates and becomes weight. And that's how Mitt, without ever really knowing why, starts writing things down. First on about anything he can find, then on envelopes rescued from the trash, finally in an unused bank ledger. Not that you would call what he writes poems—but there's no other name he can think to call them by.

And then one morning in June, just before William drives him to Jack Crider's for work (of which little paycheck Mitt's old man gets half; something about room and board), Mitt's mother, Sue, is filling his thermos and she says without turning to him that Carl Ray's number came up. He remembers his cousin as stooped, skinny, with a face featureless but for the jut of a nose and two black eyes: wet his rucksack once, on a camping trip. And now Mitt is afraid.

"His army number?" he asks Sue, already knowing that's what she means.

"Yeah—that—*lottery* number," she replies, still not quite facing him. "I saw my sister in the grocery yesterday and Big Carl Ray hurt his knee at work and Little Carl Ray's number come up." And now Mitt can hear in her voice that his mother is wondering what it will mean. "What a run of luck," says Sue.

"That right?" says Mitt. He takes a slow bite of his toast and doesn't feel like swallowing it. He sits there mute until his father, stinking the earth-and-shit stink of the barn, slams in through the front door and says that it's time to get going. The morning is still tallow-gray with night. All right, says Mitt, but forgets the thermos she filled, standing by the stove.

On the drive over, the sun is coming up in a pale, purple tangle above the treetops and he can tell it will be hot.

For a dollar fifty an hour and no chow, he and Mook Richardson work at Crider's place this summer. Today, as yesterday, and a week hence, they bale. They've been working here since a little after Mitt left school in May, a departure as unnoted and as unremarked as his arrival had been. That was when the first of the orchard grass got heavy with seed; and now in his body there is the automation, the cool, swift machinery of striking the hook into the bale and planting a gloved hand on the other end before heaving it into the wagon. Mook's eyes go glittery and blank when he works, and he won't say much of anything unless it's to call up to Crider, Is it lunch yet?

Not that it's work to talk through, but Mitt, younger by two years, doesn't talk as a rule. This morning, though, the words are working around in Mitt's skull until he can't stand not to say them. They get halfway through the first windrow before he says, "Carl Ray's number came up."

Mook plants the hook into the bale, plants his gloved left hand against the edge of the bale, hauls it all over the lip of the wagon. It is beautiful to watch. "Is that right?" says Mook. Mitt says it is. "Won the lottery, huh?" he says. Mook is tall, broad at the shoulders and spare at the waist, with knotted arms and thick legs. His face is Indian-dark and the lips are thick and the nose is long and somehow proud. Mitt says nothing. He wonders if Mook sees his future, too, and if he sees it whether it's dark clouds and black rivers and ghosts. He doesn't know how to ask.

In the truck, Crider honks the horn and Mitt watches the red slab of face making words in the side mirror.

Mook yells, "You dumb jewing bastard," but not quite loud enough.

They work through a windrow, two. The truck stops, and Jack Crider steps out from the cab, his game leg like a blind man's cane and the good one swinging out crazily to meet the soil. He hits the ground with a grimace.

"Seem like lunchtime to you?" he calls. Mitt says that it does. Mook watches him for a second before answering. "You know it does," he tells the boss.

William used to work for Jack Crider's old man, and he was there the day it happened. Lije Crider had been towing a big disc plough behind his tractor. Jack was a kid then and working out in the field with William and the rest of the hands. And Lije was pulling the disc plough and the tractor was moving with the dangerous, false slowness of big things, and his son had slipped trying to climb up in the cockpit with his father.

Didn't even know he'd run him over, William told him. You never saw so much blood, like the ground had been painted. Now Jack Crider's inherited the best spread in Texas County, three hundred acres between where Shashaw Creek flows into the Jacks Fork River: never been able to work it himself, never been able to leave it. His wife is Louellen, used to be Louellen Locke, a girl too young, too pretty for him.

They're sitting under the old apple tree that looks like a spider, dead and curled on its back. Mook is staring at Jack Crider's wife. Mitt takes a bite of white bread and bologna and watches Mook watch. He can smell hay and sweat off them, and the fertilizer.

"That's something about your cousin," says Mook, still looking at Louellen. Mitt nods assent. "You think our numbers'll come up?"

Mitt is quiet—he thinks Yes and says, "Doubt it."

"I'll tell you what I'll miss if our numbers *do* come up."

"What's that?"

"Louellen Crider," he grunts. The words give Mitt a feeling like he's recognized, walking down the street, an enemy since forgiven. He says, "Oh." And now they talk about girls they know in town, they talk a lot about the Cardinals, about a hunting trip in the fall, once the work is over. And then Louellen Crider picks up her laundry basket, hunches it against her hip and starts moving toward where the doorway splits her house like a winking eye. As she disappears into the dark fold of the door, Mook grabs his hay hook and says that he'd like to give her some of this, and then Jack Crider, who's been standing at the edge of the apple tree boughs for God knows how long, says, "You say something, Mook?"

He has a way, leg and all, of sneaking up on you while you piss, say, or scratch initials into the soft wood of his barn.

"Did you say something?" he asks again.

"Nothing," says Mook slowly, without looking at him.

"I think I did maybe heard what you said," says Crider. "I hope not, though."

"I don't think you did," says Mook, "since I didn't say."

"I think you might have said something about Mrs. Crider," says the boss. Mook is quiet. "Anyways I see it: I write your checks boy and I'm not sure you want to tell me what I have and haven't heard."

His field hand turns his gaze to him now. He says, "The checks aren't that big, Mr. Crider." He comes to his feet and swats his big hands together. He is a half a head taller than Crider, as wide at his shoulders as Crider is at the waist.

"Not big enough for you," says Crider, "you know where you can go."

Mook laughs. "That's it," he says. "I don't."

A long, shit-brown stream leaves Crider's mouth, and he shifts his weight awkwardly from off the game leg. "Anyway," he says, "that's not what I came here to talk about." He speaks for a while about gasoline, the time of day, the windrows. Around him is the sound of the hills—heat and cicadas and the moan of trees' boughs. Mitt's mind picks him up and carries him away and drops him square before Sue, filling the thermos he forgot, saying Carl Ray's number came up.

"I don't need you for the afternoon," comes Crider's voice. Mitt looks up. Like he's doing them a favor, the boss nods and goes on, "You two are done for the day."

"What?" says Mook. There is one thing, only, that Mitt hates about Mook Richardson, and that is the desperate note to his voice when it comes to matters of work and pay. Mook lives in town with his dad, in a little apartment above Key Feed and Supply. Mook's dad is a drunk, and even darker than Mook himself, and there are things about the poor house, Mitt thinks now, a kind of smell you can't wash off, that simple, happy look on his face with a twenty-dollar bill in his hand and a look of something like fear, but baser and meaner than fear, without it.

"I said," says Crider, "I don't have work for you this afternoon." He looks serious, and happy.

Mook gestures out toward the low slope and the field, all yellow-gray, and to the line of toad-colored trees and the swirls of ivy and blackberry that cut on top of the windrows.

"What in hell are you talking about?" he says. "There's enough work here for us and fifty more."

"You're not working this afternoon," says Crider. "That's that."

And so Mitt's friend hunkers down again now, plucks a piece of grass, tucks it into his lower lip.

"If you're not going to give us work," he says, "then I guess you have the decency to pay us."

"Payday's Friday," says Crider. "Tomorrow," he says.

Mook studies the grass at his feet, the field, the sun, anything but Crider himself. Jack Crider says, "Yesterday the spice man come up the road. You know how much Louellen gived him? Five dollars. Nothing but dried-up plants, I told the woman. You spent five dollars on a bunch of dried-up plants." Crider stares at Mook's shape in the grass. "Don't blame me," he says, "blame the spice man." And then Mitt is there, watching Crider make for the door that splits his house like a mocking eye.

They dredged the Jacks Fork in the '30s as part of a public works project, for the river gravel at its bottom. Years before that, the big trees on the bank had been cut down and floated past Eminence, to where the marble-green Jacks Fork meets the River, and from there, the water oozed like an infected wound on its way to the big lumber operations in Grandin. The growth now is sycamore and soft elm and poison ivy and oak, all stubborn and basically useless plants. But now, not even fifty years after the last of the big oaks and black walnuts have gone, the riverbank is a foggy welter of green and black through the red of the soil. Down the lengths of the river are the crumbling shacks of shiners, who used to come and go by canoe.

The Jacks Fork is mystery and things hidden, but it happens that the best swimming hole, where they dredged deepest and where the thicket quiets a little, is just under the new SR-114 bridge. The water is deep and the trout are moving around in the shadows, waiting, until Mook, down to his underwear, whoops and plows into the brown river. He dips below the surface and comes up again ten yards away, in the middle of the current, heading for the gray rocks on the other side. Mitt takes off the cotton tee-shirt, sweat-yellowed, the second-hand work boots, and his socks. He takes out the chicken-scratched bank ledger and the nub of pencil he uses to write in it. He takes out his empty wallet, cursing Jack Crider, and tosses it on top of the pile before wading out into the Jacks Fork. He gasps, feeling things go hard.

"Fuck Jack Crider," calls Mook now, who's propped himself up on a rock shelf at the other side. He adds, like it followed, "You're the only person I ever met who swims in his blue jeans."

Mitt shrugs. "He'll pay us tomorrow," he says.

Mook says he guesses so. "We oughta bring his lady out here," he says, standing up on the shelf. For a second, Mook looks as if he might jump in, but then changes his mind and sits back down. The grin Mook flashes at him is a queer one. In the shadow from the high bluffs, his skin is like finished wood, or like the tarnish on old silverware. He looks all of a sudden too fragile to Mitt, too human. Feeling the words begin to rush through him, he goes for his pocket, for pencil and paper. But the old ledger is on the far side of the river, with his wallet and shirt.

Later on, after Mook has died, when Mitt thinks of him he won't remember him swaying and ducking his hook in the field, or grinning at Louellen Crider or spitting his laugh at her husband—he won't remember Mook as beautiful, in other words—instead, he'll think of Mook frozen there on the rock shelf, looking weak and lonely to Mitt, who is still trying to figure out whether he wants to *be* Mook, or run the palms of his hands over him.

Mitt says that Louellen Crider seems a little slow to him, but that she's got a nice figure.

Mook says, "When you ever talked to her?"

"When've you?" Mitt says, and dips his head below the water and tries and fails to find bottom. When he comes up, Mook is still sitting there with that proprietary look on his face.

"I've talked to her."

"BS," says Mitt, but quiet.

"Huh?"

"When's your birthday?" He knows it's October, a week after his own, but it would look funny, knowing. Last Friday Mook had opened his ratty bifold and his driver's license had fallen to the ground: 10-01-1946.

"October first," says Mook.

"I'm end a September," says Mitt. "Think our numbers are going to come up—next year?"

"Maybe," Mook says. "If'n Carl Ray's did."

"Would you go?"

"Where else'd I go?" They talk about the possibilities, the length of the war, the benefits that their fathers collect from the VA. They talk about getting paid, about no work in Missouri, and then Mook says, "Might not be so bad."

"You wouldn't run?" says Mitt.

"Hell no," says Mook. "Would you?"

"No," says Mitt, who wouldn't. There's Mexico, he knows—but, no—he knows he's too much of a coward to be that kind of a coward. "But there's other things," he says now. "If you're in school."

Mook laughs. "Right," he says. "That's right."

And Mitt, trying to laugh a little, too, says, "Get married."

"Marry Louellen," says Mook. Mitt stares out over the water, toward the trees. "Push comes to shove," Mook goes on, yawning, "I'll carry a purse in there." And that's more or less how Mitt realizes that Mook doesn't care all that much whether his number does come up. It just doesn't bother him. And Mitt wants to keep something from his friend, something that will outlast what's going to happen. And for a split second the need is asphyxiating. He grabs a clump of Mook's black hair and says, "They'll make you chop this off."

And Mook doesn't say anything. The hand is there for a beat and then two, just long enough for the silence to seep in.

"You sure do smile a lot," says Mook. Then he slips off the rock shelf and into the water and paddles for the far shore.

On the other side he puts his jeans back on and calls to Mitt something about the time of day. "Let's go," he says.

All through that summer they work Crider's land for him. Mitt never touches Mook again, somehow never *wants* to. They watch Louellen Crider put up the wash, and Mitt will feel almost sorry for her husband, who must wonder, too, must think it's odd that she waits until the hands are taking lunch to set the wash out to dry.

They will drive to town at night, Mook full of big talk about finding girls. But they know all the girls here, and they know that they've been found, mostly, and they know that the ones who haven't been found— you could say they aren't really worth finding. And Mitt can't help but think that Mook understands this; that if they're serious about finding girls, then they're better off driving to Cabool or to West Plains. And Mitt can't help but notice that they never do. And Mitt wonders if Mook thinks about it like that, too.

One afternoon a hard rain falls and drives them from the yellow field. Mook, sulky about the half-pay, says, "You think about it, it's kind of you or some other sucker. Either it's your number or it's his." And Mitt is quiet.

The dog days come and Crider's fields stretch out across eternities.

One day Mook asks him, "What you're going to do in the fall?" He is holding a shovel and at the end of it is a wet, heavy load of cow shit.

Mitt gasps through his bandana, "How you mean?"

"For work," says Mook.

"I don't know," says Mitt. Strange, he hasn't even thought about it. "Help my dad, I guess."

"He need any other help?" says Mook. Mitt tries to picture his father shaking Mook's hand, cannot.

"I don't know. Kind a doubt it."

They work.

Sue starts finding chicken-scratched receipts from grocery shopping, labels torn from feed bags, on which will be written something like:

an apple tree like a spider curled up & dead, & that's where we eat

And then Mitt is helping her put away groceries and he finds the book among tins of coffee and preserving jars and canned peaches. It's leather-bound, black, with a satisfying heft to it. Mitt can feel the words moving around inside of him. He opens it and sees the blankness of its pages, and a little electric pulse moves through him.

"I thought it might fit in your jeans pocket," says Sue. Mitt stands there with a jar of peanut butter in one hand and the notebook in the other, and kind of trips over his own gratitude.

"It should fit," he tells her, and blushes, and walks into the den.

He writes. He writes about everything. He writes about Jack Crider's limp. He writes, remembering it all *perfectly*, about one afternoon, the sight of William holding his belt in his right hand, and the way it seemed for a second to thrash in the air, like a rat snake he had by the tail.

He writes about Mook, who one day calls from the gray rocks on the other side of the Jacks Fork River, he says, "Sometimes I think I might as well just join up. Better'n this shit." And Mitt looks around at the sun oozing through green trees and flashing on the rocks and the yellow rays clutching at the trout, which dodge around his legs. No, Mitt thinks, it will not be better.

Two months come and go like that. Then the sun starts swinging lower in the sky, and for not quite as long. At night, the wind is cool and smells like rotting leaves.

And at the beginning of September, too late to be called night and too early to be called morning, Mook and Mitt get a little drunk and go driving. They park Mook's truck at the end of Crider's lane and walk as quiet as thieves to the spot in front of the barn where he keeps the flatbed parked. From the boughs of the apple tree where they take lunch, Mitt watches the door and Mook buries his hayhook an inch deep in one of the tires.

It hangs there while Mook watches the tire hiss its way flat. From where he's watching, Mitt calls out low to Mook, who turns and seems to study him for an instant, seems to debate waiting there until morning. Finally, finally they take off running down Crider's lane. It should be fun, but all Mitt can think to do is wonder why he's come.

The next day, they drive to Cabool and enlist in the Army.

ESVIE COEMISH

Love Letter 32

Snapshots from the Honeymoon of Our Long Germination

Circa 18,000,000,000 BCE:

Sabbath face,
align your alien snail shell
and scuttle headlong toward your
garter-genome's ancient mating call: O
love lump in grasshoppers' night popping!
Unbinding, we pretend to summon each cell,
hollow bird eggs with pinholes at their peaks,
where holy men are left to praise bone grime,
where your fa-lalling enters like a midwife's
hook: meiosis written as a sacred book
flipped open and again whenever
your face flickers over me,
reaching out.

Circa 44,000,000 BCE:

Seismosaurus
boosts the sky on his neck,
licks God's slow dangling sandals,
but we're gnats swum inside God's eye.
X chromosomes lose legs like cockroaches
rolled in drops of forest mist with pterosaurs.
Awake now! Wake everything! You scramble
forth in our bed soup unclose to the sheer rim
of organ-brocaded flesh, a tickling machine
of touch. You print in me, love. You
are a supermoon rising, a harvest,
time's shiniest gulp of hair
misses most.

Circa 1240 CE:

Dug into
beach sand, a note
scar zoeae slog their youth
scrawling is submerged again,
ruffling beneath a herd of water
bulls, like the ones I fed bottles to,
the bean child that I was before you
pulled in my slack tide, a lunar zenith
drawing my slip straight over my head.
Read my gooseflesh in your cubbyhole
and thumb the plastic fertility goddess.
Paisley-brained, the galaxy dials seeds,
while radiation turns flesh silhouette,
but you are my sun-greased ladder.
Seagulls swoop low. Shells prick
our bare feet, and the rain is
headachy over the harbor
as tree sap liqueur
beckons.

Circa 1981 CE:

Beg aerosol
for your impregnable
still beings' fingers reaching
like the night itself, and morning
crying Father to a factory's smoke.
Your testimony drips red, blessed,
extinct ancestors whispering from
the bud that is to be your sex—
that primal cut of beauty is
a mouthful of honey.
You've evolved toward me,
belly button of my belly button,
phalangeal delta. Inside out, until
you yank the ripcord of my spine,
I luff in trancelike worldlessness.
Why was love selected as a trait?
Each wriggle from me out
into long quackgrass
shivers you.

Circa 1 UE:

Dude, your
whiskers are caught in
my windroom's pointillism.
O no? O YES! A hero breathes
one particle, and the void swoons
—for you found me in my puddle—
Let our tails coil together snakily,
the long view of the sea melting
to nebulaic beasts, all froth
and unnerved crystal,
summoning.

Born to air,
pulsars trapped inside
stern orange rocks glare on
our private parts, big and small.
Outer space is ruthless, hard. No
—for you found me in my puddle—
where, underwater, I'll spark blue
and kiss you in the ulcer-fire of
God's memo: there will be
no Adams cast from
your ribfins.

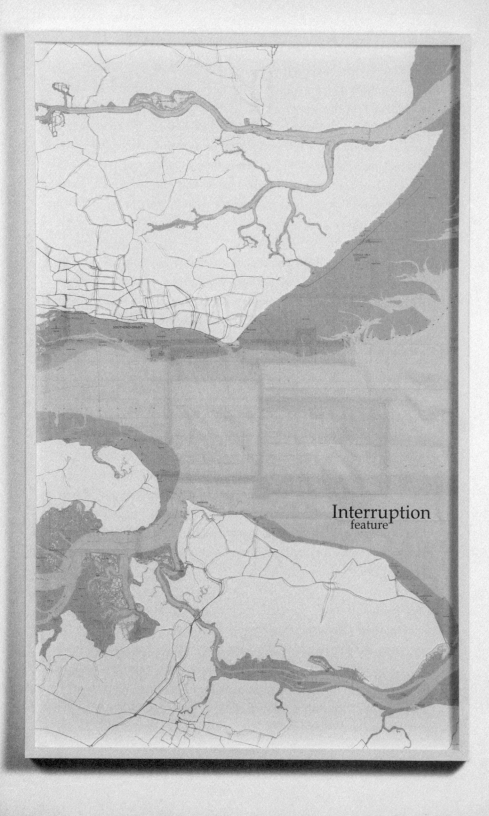

Interruption
feature

Dear Reader,

Welcome to the Interruption issue. The theme of Interrupion as the editors initially conceived it was "a moment of un-being—an arrest or hindrance of the continuity or uniformity of act, thought, writing, conversation or other discourse." In this liminal space between thought, word and utterance, we felt writers and readers would be encouraged to reformulate, reconceive and reorient in thought and speech to the world, each other and as selves. We wanted to see the "gaps in account, and we want[ed] to see the new landscapes on the page and territories of thought their articulation reveal."

These quotes are pulled whole cloth from our solicitation letter, sent to dozens of writers and artists just about a month before a category F4 tornado ripped out enormous swaths of our city. In the weeks that followed, as we diligently worked to remove debris, distribute relief supplies, and lend a hand wherever we could be of use—to each other and to our community—our theme took on a more profound and literal meaning.

It is with great pride that we offer the following pieces. We feel that each demonstrates interruption in myriad exciting ways, from artist Helen Pynor's placid underwater scenes as cradle for entire human organ systems to a main character whose grasp of the boundary between the sentient and otherwordly begin to dissolve in "Green Mountain." Karen Volkman articulates and re-articulates a landscape in "Bridge," rendering it strange and exciting time and again; and Christina Manweller spars with form and the fury and elegance of nature in "Body :: Water :: Flight :: (Fading)."

Having come through the arrest of continuity and the moment of un-being in our physical world and through the building of this book, we have seen beautiful and inspired re-articulations of thought, world, action, orientation and utterance on a daily basis for the past several months.

We hope you enjoy this document of interruption, your journey in our new-old world. Without further ado —

(The Editors)

DAWN LONSINGER

consonance

dust is the only secret
–Emily Dickinson

Removed

In 2006 a virgin komodo dragon in Chester, England, became pregnant. Newspapers called it "an evolutionary twist." Zookeepers joked about not naming any of the seven little dragons *Jesus*. Other reptile species have been documented reproducing asexually in a process known as parthenogenesis, but it had never been observed in a komodo dragon. She laid eggs. What is inside exits though there is still something veiled inside. When an egg collapsed, blood vessels and a small embryo appeared inside the fragmented. The air swooped in like a story of ending. It revealed the tissue growing in the other ovals. Like Jesus himself—alien righteousness, interjection, reverse screw. Mary shared in the gifts of the crucifixion, remained perpetually virginal, an emptied arc, mother of the untouchable. The conception is immaculate; it shines like chrome, blinds by comparison. The komodo drags her tail around the cage and dust flowers upward.

Nested

The soldiers are swathed in camouflage, but the sand is too homogenous to hide limbs. The sun is a loud and forceful music. They squint. They listen. They listen closely. Everything seems to unseam inside their ears. They think, at times, that they can hear their own blood whistling. They dig a deep line into the earth and lower themselves down into it. A burial to delay burial.

Removed

"History books forgot about us. And the bible didn't mention us, not even once."

Nested

The artist deconstructs and reorders bird nests. She is fascinated with the intricate tangle, how nothing is exactly knotted, but holds together. This is the outer womb. She tugs and everything comes undone. When she tires of rearrangement she begins to fabricate nests out of embossed aluminum strips. She calls them mirror nests. They glint in the trees. The artist asks, "What can be gleaned from paring down a thing to bits of matter and space—and the energy that moves within these?" The mirror nests are dangerous, razor-sharp.

Removed

There was a material sputtering. A chemistry of light. There was warmth and the fracturing of nearness and silence. There was roiling and accretion. When the dust settled…into a condition of unsettled dust, a single-celled organism was there. It was the upshot of a merging: one cell swallowed, imperfectly, another. Predatorial fortune: hunger, of a sort, the culprit. We are a long way from singular cells, are made up of trillions of cells though scientists are hard pressed to put an actual number on it; estimates range from 10 to 50 to 100 trillion cells per body. There is no consensus. It's hard to count with so much birth and death. So much cloak and jostle. You and I have a different number. Our fish-like organs throb in the dark. If something is inside of something is it near it? Could one, for example, say my heart and I are close? In the moment of asking this, I see in the proscenium of my mind the small papery wasp nest in the hollowed-out beam of my childhood swing set, the knot of water beside a rock in the Arno, king crabs clambering over each other in a tank that looked out onto a street, which lead to Keuomo Mountain and grew quiet—nearly 6,000 miles from here.

Nested

My voice comes up out of me, is a rope flung from a window of tissue. Who will grab it? Bastard of mucus. Anthem of letting go. Air shocked through with faction and erasure, filled with whispers.

Removed

The fact floats back. I read it. I memorize it. It clicks or falls away. A fetus develops fingerprints at eighteen weeks. Canada has more inland waters and lakes than any other country in the world. An octopus has three hearts. My amazement is endless. My distance is inevitable. The fact folds gently down like a top sheet. In 1983, a Japanese artist, Tadahiko Ogawa, made a copy of the Mona Lisa out of toast. I rub my hand across a stone I read about. It is fifteenth century. It is now. A chasm remains between my hand and my mind, between the fact and the thing. I understand its Braille in a way that burns understanding. How to explain what remains? As in a beaker after the unknown concentrate has mostly disappeared, leaving only a dusting of fine white powder, like crushed teeth.

Nested

The mummies are unwrapped. Examined. The particles tested for the trappings of time. The bones are kept approximately in place...are reconfigured to replicate place. Inside the body of bandages is absence. The organs were removed and stored in canopic jars. The skull was filled with a thick plant-based resin. Amulets against perishing. We relish and fear our capacity to save. We are trapped. Rapt in museums. At the movie theater, we scream when we hear the zombies feeding in the dark.

Removed

Somewhere incomprehensible distances away black holes are sucking light into the back of time-space's throat. This I find reassuring, that even as everything burns numberlessly, the brightness of information is being ushered away.

Nested

We saw the cell, gathered and embraced like us in its own skin. But the belly button is evidence that we are made things. That we are not hermetic, are susceptible to opening. Molecular self-assembly happens so far away right here. The nano knocks and we are always answering. Still, there is no one who can tell me how life exactly began, how matter sifted together into a movement that vibrates and sings. Into an organization that works. Into pollen pouring across landscapes, fireflies rising in unison. Into an orange poppy inside of which there is an infinity of orange poppies. It was nearly forever that the bacteria, algae, and protozoan scurried about. Alone. And now we live in a bacterial world, are constantly cutting back, wiping away, swallowing. All dressed up in virus with no place to go.

Removed

Zoos are the most obvious antidote to our subtraction by addition. What is far from us, exotic, frightening, we cull together like a sentence. But there is not a grammar that can account for this failure. Nearly all of our experiences of animals are through images. So this seems like a treat, the animals only confines away. If I was asked to draw an elephant I would forget the shape of its skull and ankles. When we get imaginative we put a horn on a horse and glitter the scene with unicorns. Extraction breeds extraction. I have been to this particular zoo three times and every time the albino crocodile is lying in the same spot in the same position with the same alarming stillness. It looks dead, especially because it appears bleached, though this is just its natural lack of pigment, probably ultimately the reason for its entrapment. Little effort has been made to recreate natural habitats. Perhaps the zoo administrators fear this would encourage wildness.

Removed

Perhaps we have pets to keep near what we know we have exiled. To train our eye on otherness. To feed something that needs to be fed and is not ourselves. To remind ourselves that the natural extends far beyond our comprehension, our experience, our vision. To be looked at by a cat. I save the gorillas for last. There are two of them, in separate cages, though there is a small circle of Plexiglas for them to look through—at each other. I imagine looking through into the eyes of the only other human, our breath fogging the peephole, our skin a tourniquet against spilling. Perhaps I love birds so much because they evade our most earnest requests, our subjugating stares, because they fly off. The gorilla seems detached, bored, cramped. He fingers through the hay for bits of carrot. I feel sick with selfishness. I would not wish away the zoo though I find it ethically bankrupt. A few years ago a tiger leapt out and mauled a man to death.

Nested

We carry in us manufactured shapes—dentures, stent, artificial eye, turbine heart, cochlear implant, hip-joint replacement. Ever editorial are our dreams. Elsewhere, diamonds are pulled up out of the earth, finagled and hustled to *mean*.

Removed

Celebrities are like animals, our relationship to them based on copies, distance. They are detached, yet seem so near to us, like brinish black olives in our mouths. A whole industry of images attests to our addiction. We chart their pregnancies and failures. Inside Madonna there is another Madonna, and inside her another, and yet another; endlessly irretrievable is the tiny Madonna at the end of matter. Others are penned in their penthouse suites and Hollywood homes and we are clambering to sic our Cerberus spotlights on them. We wish there was a feeding time, an overhead announcement that Angelina would be let out of her movies for a live performance, that we could run our fingers along her manta ray spine.

Removed

I press my thumb into the packages of cut cow tongues, watch the meat turn shades of pink and violet. This was one of my favorite things to do when I was little and bored in grocery stores, long before I became a vegetarian, long before I heard of cows being shot in the head with captive bolt pistols. I was testing the saran wrap, testing the sheen underneath of which was the severed. We went to an Amish market and pig's feet, ears, and tripe abounded. Later the vegetables looked just as alien, cut and wrapped, enormous and waxen. I grow nothing that I eat. I do not know where this or that has been, whose hands or lives it has touched. Sometimes now I am overwhelmed thinking about how every object in every store was processed in a factory, that there are people whose lives have been spent in those factories—Slim Jims, Pop-tarts, Jesus figurines, playing cards, toothbrushes, trinket, trinket, trinket. I picture the molds, the machinery. I picture piles of defective meat. I picture sugar falling all around us.

Nested

Inside architecture we arrange and breathe. It is a breeding ground of scaffolding and objects. It is a haunt. If we could peel back the façade we would see ourselves enclosed in piping and electrical wire. We would see how softly we settle into gravity. How we are only momentarily suspending this particular scene with these particular things. How we stockpile against disappearance. If it weren't for all of these books this room might drift off. I move things around, try to even out the ballast. It is a vessel with many tiny vessels—bright candy dish, pill box, milk swaying in its carton, bowl stacked inside bowl. In one high-rise hundreds of identical canisters of comfort, of somewhere-here. Hundreds of televisions with unsleeping cathode ray tubes—electron guns inside evacuated glass envelopes. Hundreds of vacuum cleaners with guts of debris. Hundreds of pots and pans. At night skyscrapers are empty abdomens of light, modern-day spires, glass stained with the thump and fall of birds.

Removed

"Not one would mind, neither bird nor tree
If mankind perished utterly;
And Spring herself, when she woke at dawn,
Would scarcely know that we were gone."

Nested

I have a strange conception of pregnancy. I have generally and vaguely imagined that I would have kids. But when I really think about it, about pregnancy in particular it kind of freaks me out. My ex tells me his mother once had a dream about giving birth to an alien cat baby. Though I can't quite negotiate the space between cat and baby, I am calmed by this. Perhaps I am not the only woman who doesn't feel like her insides are full of a damp earth waiting for roots. It's not so much that I don't feel

motherly, because sometimes I do, but that I find it profoundly disturbing
to think of this thing (i.e., the baby) growing inside of me without effort,
without consent even. Of course by this logic I might also consider my
brain alien, if it wasn't producing these very thoughts, if I wasn't at risk of
being diminished to mere tautology. Nonetheless, I can't help but think
of a fetus as an alien, that it will feel alien, that it will feel like an intrusion
to have my body suddenly stretched like an echo. Of course, it does not
help at all that fetuses look like aliens, or rather, that we have decided to
create an iconography of aliens that look like fetuses, eyes stretched wide,
fingers webbed, parts growing upon parts. When I see a near-mother
with her hands on her distended belly I wonder—does she really feel
close to it-not-yet-him-or-her? Is it any different than all the other things
that happen inside the body unannounced? Are its sweet little kicks just
electrical? Are we toaster-ovens? I will know it is eating what I am eating.
I will know that it is reliant, conditional, becoming present.

Removed

I needed to imagine the body of God as a body not yet broken into, not
yet wisping away. I started to notice the remarkable resemblance between
Santa Claus and God. This before I knew that my parents were Santa
Claus. For many this may have been a comfort. Instead it fucked with my
expectations. Who was I praying to? Who was bringing presents? Who
was watching me? I comforted myself with small, clear distinctions and
truths. For example, God was less rotund and more lit up, and Santa
Claus less wind-blown and more jolly. For example, superpowers, I could
discern, belonged to men, old white men. This, I concluded, must be
why old white men were kings. Once I learned of satyrs and centaurs
and phoenixes rising up from nests of fire there was no going back to
that whole born into punishment *Scarlet Letter* bit. He/It/God was too
remote. I couldn't picture the uncontainable God of creation containing
Himself within. These multiform creatures seemed, paradoxically,
more consistent and familiar. And gods plural seemed more viable, more
inclusive, more egalitarian, more fun. Still, when my neighbor took me
into the church graveyard after summer Sunday school and told me to
ask Jesus into my heart, I did. I pictured him swimming around in my

arteries, drawing ♥s on the walls. I thought about how I wouldn't know one way or another if he was in there. I stared at the stone tablets, the deep cut of the letters belonging to people I did not, and would not, know. Dandelions were crushed beneath my feet. It was humid, and the air smelled sweetly of live things. The moon glowed in its far-off orbit.

Nested

Computers offer us a lovely leakless ether, a system of signs that is "everywhere" accessible. A nest of numbers. A clustering operation. Nodes can no longer be thought of as individual. We are distortion-oriented. Do we glide through the information space or does the information sashay through us? Is it reciprocal? When did you first become involved with your computer? How often do you see each other? There are things inside that I cannot understand, scaffolding that I cannot witness. Does it preserve the important tensions? How to support emerging structures? How to insure that emerging structures represent the vast multiplicity of thought? Will computer language, like other languages, constrain us to certain modes of thought, to certain ways of perceiving, to widespread immobility? I click and excavate. I cut and paste. Sometimes there is a sudden system failure. Sometimes things flicker in and out. Sometimes I want to wad clay around all of my joints.

Nested

The frame makes a pool of our faces. We are a family represented as a family. We are over there. We are viewable at a distance. We can fit in my pocket. Locket for those who are gone. The air in the ambulance is balmy yet stale; the patient is strapped to the stretcher as the whole of the instant curves through the streets like a needle sewing up the night. The sound of emergency is faint, like a lullaby.

Removed

I open the paper and fifty-one more are dead. It is as if my casual morning read has caused this. I am reminded of my ineffective nature, of my smallness. Of our enduring cruelty. The US government sends life-size cardboard replicas of active duty soldiers to their families. These are meant to curb the severe sense of abandonment felt by their children, to portray less distance. The cut-outs are called Flat Daddys. One mom props her husband's six-foot cut-out by the swing set while her son plays. Another puts hers on the couch and covers him with a blanket. It is a visual operation.

Nested

Cuttlefish have three basic camouflage templates—uniform, mottled, and disruptive. "The animal's magic is looking at a complex visual scene and only picking out the one or two visual clues to turn themselves into the most discrete pattern." The diving biologist enters the ocean thousands of times. The ocean is so touchy-feely, primordial, unbreathable. Creatures are lifted into labs, placed gently into tubs, into viewing domes. But only in the ocean can they observe the true visual of predator-prey interactions. The octopus is a maven of disguise. It sinks into its environment like water itself. It sways like kelp in the tide. It is not until the camera nearly touches it that it gives up cover, flashes like a god into a heifer, a poplar, a renegade planet.

Nested

From trees we extract maple sap in buckets...or pipelines are placed so the sap is pulled down by gravity into the sugar house. I like to think of the heart as the sugar house of the body though it looks most like a bloody fist. Open the hood of your car and hear the humming sputter. I peel an egg and eat it. The yolk dissolves in my mouth. The ballerina always rises and twirls. The mayflies shake their skin like a gown after a party, fever pitch mate in the sweltering air. At night, in the bourbon darkness, I pull the covers over me, even when it's oppressively hot.

Removed

At the *Body Worlds* exhibit, the plastinated bodies are no longer the bodies of individuals. The donation is complete. The scientist-cum-artist has taken liberties, has turned non-runners into runners, has left the testicles attached but peeled back the breast. There's a Michelangelo imitation, skin in hand, the hair hanging on. And "The Capillary Family," the blood vessels maintained, everything else vibrated away. The blood child sits on the blood mother's shoulders. The blood father's braided wrist touches the blood mother's bundled waist. They (remnant & object) stand there behind glass, made of the apple red ramblings of the heart. A plaque informs us that "laid end to end, all the blood vessels in a human body would encircle the earth twice." Who here can do multiplication? I think of rivers bleeding out into valleys, of electrical networks of neurons. In a nearby display case is the circulatory system of a chicken in the shape of a chicken. It's true: when we move we tow along entanglements—

Removed

The umbilical is cut. The planets don't touch. The mall remains. Dollywood remains. Languages are fading into extinction. We are uninvolved even while we are involved. And vice versa. New Orleans. Afghanistan. Egypt. Say a place and try not to touch it. My students argue that they themselves have not benefited from slavery. Slavery and dinosaurs are moderated by the repeated utterance, by the lack of pause. Slavery. Dinosaurs. Slavery. Dinosaurs. They sound like a story, but the bones holler back. The air is thick with vestige, what is lost swelling inside of fruit. Bodies have been dropped from planes. People and cities have disappeared much more quickly than anyone thought possible, except for those who did exactly that—thought it possible, thought oblivion. When honeybees and bats began to disappear, a movie was made of this disappearance.

Nested

Take, as evidence of the bewilderment of form, the turducken: a partially deboned turkey stuffed with a deboned duck which itself is stuffed with a small deboned chicken. The thoracic cavity of the chicken and the rest of the gaps are sometimes stuffed with a highly seasoned breadcrumb mixture or sausage meat. Take, as evidence of the exhaustion of forms of subjugation, this: the largest recorded nested bird roast included seventeen birds, attributed to a royal feast in France in the early nineteenth century (originally called a *Rôti Sans Pareil,* or "roast without equal")—a garden warbler stuffed into an ortolan bunting, into a lark, into a thrush, into a quail, into a lapwing, into a plover, into a partridge, into a woodcock, into a teal, into a guinea fowl, into a duck, into a chicken, into a pheasant, into a goose, into a turkey, all nestled inside of a bustard. The garden warbler, the final bird to be stuffed, is so small that it can only be stuffed with a single olive.

Removed

Rain fills the acoustic darkness. Rain tries to touch us but gets only so far as the window, blurs. It impersonates desire, cuts us off and envelops us, sinks in. There is always debris. We must start from there. The rain sounds sticky, as if tugged through something. The tissues in the tissue box are folded into each other so that each one gently touches the last as it leaves. Outside, near-relic telephone wires map our bonds across the earth, how bound up in the voices of the departed we are. Except these wires are lifted up, at a distance, as if touch were impossible or dangerous. If and when we lift up off the earth, the cabin is pressurized.

Nested

I spent many childhood summers visiting my great-grandparents in Sea Isle City, NJ. Land hugged by water, which was hugged, far out beyond where any of us could see, by land. My great-grandfather had deer-like eyes and rocked in his rocking chair, with baseball on the TV, humming, just rocking and humming. My grandmother was, as I remember her from the vantage of smallness, warm, plump, talkative. She wore dull dresses with tiny flower patterns, and always had her hands in something—dishwater, freezer, dough, meatloaf, dirt. There was the inevitable commentary on how she couldn't believe how much I looked like my mother—"that's Barbie, alright; look at her, just look at her, a spitting image." An image that spits itself? My mother recognizable in me? I remember the smell of age and molasses in that small house, and how all we wanted was to run off, to go to the ocean and never leave it; we could feel its pull from blocks away, taste the enticement of salt in the air. Oh, the waiting in that small house for that big thing, waiting in that house of shells. There was nowhere that shells had not reached—on the soap dish, on top of doilies on top of nightstands, lining window ledges, mixed in with costume jewelry, in blue bowls around the living room, along the walkway leading up to the porch, bits of them ground into the carpet. Outside, the house was encircled with spiky conch shells. These were my favorite. These you could hold up to your ear and hear the ocean. I believed in that magic, big thing haunting the little thing which used to live inside of it. Echo of that which lived inside a shell; echo of emptiness. Seashells making ocean sounds. Oceans churning seashells. Later, I would spend nights with a man who listens to the sound of the ocean from his iPod in order to fall asleep.

Removed

The older I get the more I feel myself tapering, various selves giving up the ghost. Once, there was light and me in it. Then bed times, then classrooms, then work, then catastrophe legible and boundless. There's no pollen on my wrists, no trigonometry in my brain. I am becoming specialized.

Nested

Is the spiral jetty a deformity on the picturesque landscape? The spiral pulls the landscape into it; the spiral spews everything out. I begin and walk inward, then back again. Either its beginnings are everywhere, being connected as it is to the shore, or its endings are everywhere.

Nested

I practice at translation, representation, the art of naming loss—which is here, with us, in the air, as the distance between your shoulders. What kind of womb is this room? What kind of cosmos? What kind of connection? Rupture? Here where the breath of another just seeped into you, where dispersal is imminent, where simultaneity smolders. There is the distance between us. Our mouths can barely keep themselves from trying to correct this—word word word, swallow swallow, kiss. There is the distance between us, and it's material.

Removed

I once read somewhere that when a woman looks at her naked self in the mirror she never looks at herself from her own perspective, always from the perspective of those she imagines will look nakedly at her.

Removed

When I smile at you I flash my teeth, my skull. Perhaps this is why smiling is a sign of affection or happiness—I am saying, "Look, death, which seems so far off, is in me too."

Nested

In the heart of joy is the heron of loss, and in the heron of loss a skull of beauty. Where are you shelterless? We should stop mid-sentence before the wars start up again. You are at the very center of some version of all of this. Inside, a glass-like silence. Outside, mounds of broken glass. When I wade out into the ocean, my brain alone can't get wet, cool off. It is alone in its own ocean, trawling an electric lace that ties everything, absolutely everything, together. When I say ham, you can kind of taste it, no? Rain, and rain is upon us, inside. And so I say whale song ::: egg ::: clove :: red velvet :: plume of smoke :: dew. You say it with me, nested as you are in this, or you don't, distant as you are in your exquisite scenic elsewhere.

ZACHARY SCHOMBURG

Miner Death

This time when I come out of the mine, I step immediately into another mine. The world has finally become what I knew it would become, a series of endlessly interconnected mines. I am a thought or a disease. That is my new sad lot in life. You open your mouth. A bright circle of countryside is out of it.

Casting Out the King of Boys

On my last day as king, I watched a dirty movie behind the couch. My father said I should get used to that sort of thing. I ate every last possible meal in the refrigerator. Those were great memories from someone exactly like me's childhood. Now I am in a field, I am part of the field, like a poppy, in my pretty dress. There is nothing larger to grow into.

SHELLY TAYLOR

[5]

Johnson & Johnson in the outlet hub: you have always done me well.
To love a house is to touch it, all over, & to have a phone that does
things resembling his every movement—hello? I went a long time
feeling nothing & everything at once but my face held up well
in retrospect, these bitters full & bad things we do to ourselves
in our 20s; yes I've wiped the house down ten times today &
every house I've lived in since I had my own. Ever feel you too ate &
drank the house down like I did last summer, Grita?—yellow curtain
flutter the wall, a bleached down pallor I take to with spray here,
paper towel there. You have everything, all that, behind you & it was
not-good & good both. I think now only present the way a child can,
& neither do I want a bath or the linear world I'm supposed to
sashay through a lady. We fought the silence, the men inside us—
through the tunnel for the field I imagine myself a member of
the National Football League—the day leaned hard into what
I thought would work me, semblance of a melody, desert
cold imperceptible to touch, as in you were watchful as a child,
sharp notes. I might've stayed by that stingray tank all my life,
hell I still might be there, pigtails, them brushing past my fingers,
softest bellies, mother telling him impatient to go on;
her waiting for my fill. Short-handed, I'm there still, smooth bellies
—your eyes in your jersey, NFL longings, yes,
the day with waiting. How we bust ourselves open
for each other; your mother, hesitancy in all you touch now
after her. I waited x years for him to get me, I became older: it hurt,

it hurt. I grow regimental good soldier: you are not your mother's
life vestment, man hands in the dark, walk 'til the world
lights the dirt streets, the tussled held in your lifetime, always inside
you growing still, for your life would be a mysterious droll,
uncommon. And this will one day be yours, we tell the unbirthed,
when your child hands grow outwards. Hardnosed, presto, a thaw,
so much demand on daylight, for whom small deaths are emphasized
& something to think hard of, animal-like in its internal posture,
not my belly, further out & speaking loudly, ours. I am not the skin of
the fine woman you take me for: tell your man
to ready for blood, enigmatic sprung forth out the clay streets or
rifled Mantanzas balcony—the sunset awful pink & night stars
coming on all shoulders which sag the way shoulders do when
bereft carrying on; lip twitch on the balcony,
world long whippoorwill. This war that sits atop his chest
usually after dark, I tell follow instructions, mutely. His or hers, &
their upbringers. But his face is laced with mud, whiskey
leaking behind a tire—his summer & life for your kingdom forever.
I mute the ragtime from its station out of Jacksonville, turned to
the weather so it would not just be me here. See, I've
never thought much about a child 'til you sallied forth; Jane or Betty,
leave the demons to God—I'll collect her help you. Nobody
writes about love anymore, either it hurts too bad the heart or either
you're just so damn happy you write the river birds which are black
smut. Sayso now, as far as you go, to the gunman, the gunman,

anger in the thoroughfare, your local grocery store & a kid

with a gun going mad on the lot. The world needs more love poems

& love to work, call Mr. Creeley back fast or cover your life. But this

is all noir. He crawls a street & fire is in a city window threatening the

whole building & we jump off a bridge something like the Manhattan

passing into Chinatown, rapido. The tenement only occurs

in my dreams in a place I'd never allow myself live again for fear of

backwards. And see here baby whom I pray is a girl, none of this

has nothing to do with you yet, therefore accord no merit.

[7]

The beach gives onlookers, men with poles. I am just trying to jog
this beach, if I yelled you fucking voyeur it would not be got. I liken
myself to Faulkner's going on about nature while being sharp
with the two characters of this working—you know, & God always God
let's call him Higher Power the way the Al-Anon book says.
In the past you were shot at, mid-hand dealt as if shuffle inward yet
leave it alone. I drink a Mich Ultra, that's what in the fridge. And
slow to the gunny, the time spent I drug myself by belly, slept
when the sun came up, my hands back again. A picture
of you, ain't it funny, in the bar forever, my good tap tap, fingers
& feet now I've no speedrack, five hundred bottles a night, two
in each hand & this is Heaven. But your hands in my hair,
a periodic newness for remembrance which like a shrug dully evokes
the winter coming. I have my graces from which
I carry the sun to violence all my mistakes, born into thick hands,
cruelty & choose so. If I curl my hair I'm taking on the town,
the real of the town, everyone with their beer whiskey hands all sad
behind their beer whiskey hands, you cannot run it down—plié & shade
from any ray that looks you step right because right cannot tell
the difference between a marsh & a swamp: we kill both. I thought
go home again & it was murky, the sea unfledged, myself
in the backyard watching closely the cats
don't jump the fence & get out there on the road.

[17]

Unseemly, would you accept his ghost denied access,

likewise the men God make so reprobate, backbiters, etcetera,

pure meats. Standfast holding, holding through his blood,

rebelieve yourself in man's flesh though she needn't a man's touch;

Willie Nelson to the curve, hers is glamour, farmer, working it like

nightbirds black under the moonlight, work clothes; I do things for

women reasons, stripped down to a wedding dress—base it on

the funk pimp, the dirrrty, lawn chairs out on the front yard, her

bourgeoning need to strike out unmarried: you won't know

all she put in it. There is water I wrenched against, there is mine

& that which will forever elude, eyes hazel hard to grasp, you just

cannot. Home of the built right, I went glossy to get a stake in life

as perpetual, as in liquid, the house that is home from a magazine you

wanna sink it's all lilacs & too assumed—so as to keep myself up on it.

You get what you ask for. I want it girded for the foxes,

something to still the sea's waves, these 20s something bitters

I say my vows nightly (flit south tiny bird with its two eyes

trading off) Jesus, Jesus who had no sister. Please keep his body

upright so no downward he could spiral, walk out

a lion, bones for not living, earphones to stay the world be here.

He smarts on the inside, his war wounds smart his very body

at the center, he bends as if shot, what! His glock stays his pocket

cause his right hand is a falsehood. All man's is likened to a vanity,

you anger him, he gets a bigger voice, for he is not really home,

good men in harmony, harmony—the powers that be

Jesus walking, like. I will hustle. That's the way women do things. Now brutish walking the red road Georgia, because my feet know how to shape it rightly innovation, my dirty feet abide my house.

[20]

When proxy all night I poured Jack into
the morning. Heat makes the dogs heave
on the porch, blue the roof
to dissuade dirt daubers from home-making—
& ramshackle that which keeps him well-nourished,
High Life, his Redbreast. Hourglass round
the steakhouse, if I started up again no one could
keep me from trying, all night a rodeo, all morning
rye grass, water to paw I could roll into your body
to keep me safe not sage, but the longing,
the still of incomprehension, the bottles from
the speedrack I drove off another night bruised legs &
G Straited myself right again, all Jäger down my arms,
whiskey arms & all over my britches, you could
punch the eye of. A homemade mother
never washing dishes, such gentle hands, nutshells
across the floor, left your boots that lasted
three tours to the monsoon, mama,
her boy, my boy, her dissolute sadness.

Elizabeth Hall

Green Mountain

10/15/1939

Rain. Red mud gushing up, glutting the windshield. To see at all, Lara must lean forward, grip the wheel. Perched atop a steep hill, the Inn is only accessible via a single-lane dirt road. She drives no faster than thirty, rounds each curve with the utmost care—still she spins out. Eases the car from the ditch, fixes the tire. Up up up the hills, down a gravel driveway. The Inn: shrouded by seven pines, four waxy shrubs; yard otherwise cleared off save an unpainted wooden fence, smattering of pigs, three cows, a lone chicken wailing. No sooner has she parked the car than William, one of the Inn's owners, taps on the driver's window *wonderful weather, eh?*

A suitcase in each hand, they walk across the sagging porch steps. Crusted oriental rugs line the lobby, which is really an over-sized living room. Vaguely floral wallpaper, a plush red davenport; silk hyacinths shoved into mason jars, jars scattered across the mantle, couch-side tables. William introduces her to his twin brother Horatio who extends his hand *we own the Inn with our sister Mary.* Horatio gestures towards a woman seated behind an engraved desk. Sliding the room key across the desk, Mary smiles *most of our other guests are still asleep. Dinner will be served at eleven PM.* Lara asks *eleven?* Mary nods *eleven.* Lara signs the guest book using the alias assigned to her by the paper: Billie Lassiter, age 27, Houston, TX. From his perch at the top of the stairs, Horatio stares down at her. Stares with persistence *I'll show you to your room.* Located at the far end of the second story, her room has but one window, overlooking the pig pen. Horatio apologizes about the weather, his attire *we don't normally dress like this. It's just the pigs been getting...we'll see you at dinner, eh?* She says *yes* then shuts the door.

Although, alone in the room, Lara cannot shake the feeling of Horatio's gaze. It creeps across her face, slopes down her back and legs. She snaps the blinds shut, closes the curtains. The only light in the room comes from the crack beneath the door. Two hours pass. Lara sits on the bed in silence. Worn from the drive, it will take all her might to attend dinner. Intestines ache at the mere thought of digestion. Head swarms at the first sounds of the other guests waking, staggering down the hall towards the communal bathroom. 9:43 PM. Countless flushes, insistent knocks, water from the tap, a woman sighing *it's so early, far too early.* In her journal, Lara records all that she hears and smells—what little she can see through the crack at the bottom of the door, writes even about Horatio's "gaze" knowing Mr. Hammonds, her boss at the paper, will twist his face *aww shit how many times have I told you.* Someone knocks on the door. Her whole body stiffens, refuses to soften even as she answers the voice *what is it?* A man says *dinner in five minutes.*

Still, Lara shakes. In the foyer she stops to rest, leans her head against a massive flower pot. Her breathing slows enough for her to walk down a small set of carpeted steps into the dining room. The guests fall silent. William grabs her hand *come, honey, take a seat already.* Lara sits next to a woman named Caroline and her husband Harold who are drinking gin fizzes, grinning through the liquor *we're from Cali-forn-ia.* They toast. Twenty guests total. Most from far-away, out West or the Plains. Lara drains her gin, asks Caroline *what brings you to the area?* Aside from the Inn, there are no attractions of any sort for at least fifty miles. No vistas or hiking trails. The only reason for booking a room: seclusion. Horatio emerges from the kitchen with a 16 lb. smoked ham; the table sags beneath its weight. Some guests eat ravenously while others dawdle, lingering over the broccoli. At the precise moment Lara realizes she can eat no more, Mary sweeps her plate from the table in a single, effortless gesture—almost unperceivable. William eyes Mary briefly, then noticing Lara eyeing him, turns the opposite direction.

Dismissed from dinner, Lara returns to her room, although it's apparent by the noise downstairs that there is a gathering. She is not invited. Using the hall telephone, she dials Mr. Hammonds' number. No answer.

Mr. Hammonds is famous in Houston, and only Houston. Famous by trade: tabloids. He owns several more reputable print outlets but none have garnered the public affection and rage as *The Houston Bullet*. Lara once worked for his most prestigious paper *The Houston Post;* however, a single incorrect fact landed her in the over-stuffed leather chair opposite his desk. Ten, twenty minutes he stared her down, informed her that never, not even once, had *The Post* printed a retraction *but with you, that's what we had to do.* He sat down behind his desk *I've got your new assignment. For* The Bullet. *You know,* The Bullet? Of course, Lara knew: she was being punished, exiled. The Bullet? *Are you kidding?* Mr. Hammonds said *it's not that you made a mistake but that you made a willful mistake. Sympathizing with your subjects won't get you anywhere.*

Prior to his role as print tycoon, Mr. Hammonds was a hustler in San Antonio, and although he tried, he never lost the look. Clad in his swagger-suit, he rubbed his paunch then lit his pipe *aw you're a tough girl, Lara. You've done worse assignments before.* Inhaling hard, he coughed—*look, I've heard a lot of stuff about this inn up in Vermont. Write your piece on whatever you see. Or think you see.* Standing from her chair, hands on her hips *Vermont, really?* He motioned for Lara to sit, did not so much as pause *under normal circumstances we would never send a woman on this sort of story. 1,689 miles. The drive will be good for your head. Clean out all the riff-raff.* Without waiting to hear her answer, he handed her a big blue envelope with the details, a set of keys, and said *call when you get there.*

More noise from downstairs. Noise straight on until four AM, then, silence. Lara tiptoes from her room and peers into the empty lobby. Descends the stairs, holding her breath, her entire body close. Two steps down the hall, she is stopped by William *ah Mrs. Lassiter we thought you were asleep.* She stuttered *sleeping pills, I've taken and can't find the kitchen.* Something about water, yes water. William says *there's a cooler upstairs, outside the bathroom.* He leads her back upstairs, hand on her shoulder *goodnight, Mrs. Lassiter.*

*

10/17/1939

At dawn Lara is the only one awake save Horatio. Six AM: he feeds the pigs, fills two red troughs with two buckets of slop. Chickens peck at his boots for bits of corn, straw, stray twigs, or simply just to peck. Although she does not know why, she feels a great sense of calm watching Horatio latch the gate, walk across the lawn. The entire Inn dead quiet. The kind of silence that makes *all thoughts* possible.

Do the twins know she is a reporter? It's as if William and Horatio take specific pleasure in upholding the charade; a wide grin, wink, and wave as they say her name with ridiculous emphasis *o yes Ms. BILLIE o yes we have lived here our entire life anything else Ms. BILLIE?* She no longer bothers asking the guests questions, certainly not what happens downstairs, after hours. Standing in line for the bathroom, the woman from Detroit blinks *nothing.* Her husband *nothing.* The guests in room 108, 116, 210 *nothing.* At dinner the singer from NYC studies her reflection in the silver slit of a butter knife; Lara asks *with all the lovely places to stay, why Green Mountain?* The singer balances the knife on the edge of her plate *the sleep, the silence.* (Which, sure, plausible enough: why should such a simple act as watching Horatio feed the pigs soothe her so? Why does she wake later and later every morning?) If the Inn's activities are not a hoax then certainly something illicit. Gun running? Gambling? Liquor sales?

What she cannot quite admit: since arriving, she finds it increasingly difficult to differentiate between what she hears and sees and what she merely thinks. No matter how many nights she spends stretched out on the carpet, ear pressed to the floorboards, listening for a clue, she never gets any closer.

*

10/19/1939

Dear Mr. Hammond's,

I have written this letter without premeditation or revision. For if I were to "meditate," I would say nothing at all.

Unstable? Insane? Is that what you will think? When I say that yes, some "strange stuff" has happened at the Inn. From the second I set foot on the front porch *I knew*. Although it was nearly 7 PM when I checked in, the other guests were "still asleep." dinner was not served till almost midnight every night. While odd, these facts alone implicated nothing save the quaint quirkiness of the owners, which, at first glance: bumpkins. The siblings wore matching overalls, encrusted muck-boots. My room was commonplace: double bed, cracked nightstand, lamp with green shade, a single window, brittle lace curtains. Sure, the innkeepers seemed always to be watching, studying my every gesture—so what? by the fourth day I had convinced myself that I was "crazy" or, to use your exact phrase, "unstable." you ignored—no, mocked—my report of the bizarre activities I witnessed downstairs my first night after the other guests thought I was asleep. "Out of my mind," you said, "this is your last chance."

I have, in one way or another, stumbled upon "the story." the most immaculate narrative arc. The "dirt"? Twin mystics. No, twin psychics. Levitation, hand-less healing, all the BS minus snake handling. What's more—the "proof" is in order. Notes, interviews, and pictures, all legit, sealed-n-shipped. If you would like the exclusive scoop, I expect "grovel" and "beg."

Sleeplessly Yrs,

Billie

*

10/19/1939

The guests had barely finished their soup when Lara slipped out of dinner. The rug at the head of the hall was bunched up, and although she kicked it twice, it budged none. The wallpaper had the opposite effect: it looked as if it would at any moment melt off the wall. Throughout the afternoon, and especially dinner, she had felt that if she did not get in touch with Mr. Hammonds soon, she would lose it forever even if she was unsure what that "it" might be.

All her thoughts circled back: since arriving at the Inn, Lara slept. No matter that she was a lifelong insomniac. And not just any sleep: out. Dead to the world. Even more unsettling: the cloying tenderness she felt toward the Inn, or had begun to feel. She tried to focus on the facts, write in her journal, yet no matter how detailed her descriptions, nothing made sense. Although she had already decided to leave the next morning, she needed the reassurance of Mr. Hammonds' *yes, come.*

The hallway was narrow, too narrow to accommodate more than one body at a time unless single file. Inside the coat closet, the phone. No sooner had she dialed Mr. Hammonds' number, Horatio appeared. His shoulders filled the doorframe *busy tonight, eh?* She hung up. He said *join us downstairs tonight if you wish but, right now, go to your room and sleep. I'll wake you when its time.* What had changed? Lara sat in the very center of the bed and scoured the details, and at some point, fell asleep. Horatio knocked on the door, said *Billie Billie Billie.* She opened her eyes, slipped on her shoes, and followed him downstairs, toward a door at the end of the hall that she had never noticed before. Touching the door with his fingertips, and just the tips, it opened.

The room was small, dim-lit, somehow red, like the inside of an eyelid. Horatio instructed Lara to sit on one of the cracked wooden benches. In the left corner, a thumping. She was unable to place the source of the thumping, and within seconds, it was accompanied by the sound of a man panting. Although it was still spring, the room sweltered. Impenetrable stench of sweat. Lara felt close to each and every person in the room, impossible not to. A purple light flashed. A bodiless voice began to communicate in Portuguese, and although she knew no language but her own, she *knew.* All the guests understood what the voice had said as the voice did not speak so much as convey. They listened, obedient. The purple light flashed again, shone bright, then burned out. More and more bodiless voices rose up. Voices like bees wearing coats. A total annihilation of the senses. Lara could not distinguish between surfaces: the bench, wall, bodies. The first spirit she witnessed sidled close to her. Unable to see it, she could feel it around her body. She said *you do not exist.* She breathed deep, sniffed the air around her to make sure she was still in the room, not alone *I do not believe that you exist.* The spirit replied *that is of no concern to me.*

The spirit seemed to know her as she knew it, completely. It was as if her body, her very skull, had been emptied out. The spirit stayed at her side. Six hours passed. She thought nothing. Six hours? It felt like NO TIME. She sat on the bench, staring straight ahead.

Still in her soaked shirt and skirt, she unlocked the door to her room, collapsed onto her bed, every limb tingling. She slept as if never before. She returned the next night. And the next.

*

10/23/1939

Dearest Lara,

send the article ASAP or R.I.P

Yours Truly,
grovel AND beg

*

POSTMARKED: 10/27/1939

THE UNREPORTED HISTORY OF THE GABBLE BROTHERS: A PERSONAL ACCOUNT
By Lara Stein

Two boys born twelve minutes after midnight. A harvest moon. The boys did not scream, not even a single cry. Their mother Julia asked *are they dead?* The doctor laughed as he wrapped the wiggling babies in blue blankets. Zep, their father, stared out the only window in the room *I thought they were supposed to cry.*

Two boys: Horatio and William. As grown men 6'6" and thick—not fat—*big*. Big to the extent their bodies generated their own heat. They "occupied" a room. As toddlers, though, they dominated no space. Small, silent things—eyes glazed, faces slicked with dew as if in a trance. For hours at a time, with no premeditation or control, Horatio and William dropped out.

Shortly after the twins' birth, strange poundings began shaking the walls of the single-story shanty in which the Gabbles lived. Disembodied voices could be heard in empty rooms, and occasionally, the children even vanished from their cribs only to be found anywhere, even outside, perched high in a tree. As the boys grew older, their unexplained powers strengthened. Unexplained: Julia knew. A descendant of a long line of psychics, Julia's great-great-great-grandmother was killed in the 1692 Salem witch trials. Grandfather Petty, gifted with "second sight," was mortally beaten on his farm for "the devil's doings." Known for her "astonishingly accurate" predictions and visions, Julia had long hidden her talents ever since Zep cornered her on the sidewalk in broad daylight *devil! devil!* In her diary from the time, Julia wrote *he never apologized.* Discovering herself to be with child, the couple cooed *I do.* Packed what little they owned into Zep's burned-out wagon and headed north to New Hampshire.

Located on the fringes of a barren apple farm, the Gabbles' clapboard overlooked nothing. In the winter, monstrous snow. Zep's temper peaked. After bruising his hand during William's last beating, he ordered both boys, who were in a trance, to stand outside without shoes. In school, invisible hands threw books, levitated desks, sent rulers, pencils, and slates flying through the room. At this stage the boys—still so very small, their black hair more like fuzz—had little to no control of their powers or the loose spirits that accompanied their presence. After seeking the guidance of a good christian friend, Zep sold the twins to a traveling showman. $50 each. For the next fourteen years, Horatio and William were beaten, stoned, shot at, spit upon all over America, Canada, and Europe. When their father finally died, the contract with the showman was annulled. The boys returned to New England to live with their spinster sister Mary on her farm in Green Mountain, Vermont. Owned and operated by Horatio, William, and Mary, the Green Mountain Inn is known nationwide for one thing alone: "spooky stuff."

In the back corner of the house is a circular room outfitted with nothing save three benches and a small cabinet. The room is small and unventilated with only one way in or out. After conducting a thorough search, no secret closets, panels, latches, trapdoors, or any other sort of "trickery" was found. Likewise, I arrived at the Green Mountain Inn without any reason to believe. I left, not in a state of unbelief, but a state in which believing or unbelieving was wholly irrelevant. To try to *know* a thing, understand its every element, is to kill it.

Every night of the week the guests gathered downstairs in the foyer to prepare themselves for the séance. Preparations were limited: remove shoes and "suspend judgment." In the center of the room, a platform was lit by a single kerosene lamp, recessed in a barrel. William, who acted as the primary medium, mounted the platform and entered the cabinet. Voices began to whisper, first at a distance, then closer and closer. Often, there was singing, accompanied by spectral music. Disembodied hands appeared, caressed the guests' heads and necks. The first spirit emerged from the cabinet. One cannot always *see* the spirit but one *feels* it. The spirit may or may not speak, but the spirit always *touches*. A tingling at the top of the spine, spidering out to every extremity. Over the course of an evening, twenty or thirty spirits might appear. Some completely visible, others almost transparent. Ranging in size from over six feet to only three, the spirits ranged in nationality and spoke many different languages. The spirits often performed, sang, and became "intimate" with the guests. During my stay I witnessed nearly every type of supernatural phenomena: rappings, moving physical objects, spirit paintings, automatic writing, prophecy, speaking in tongues, healings, unseen voices, levitation, remote visions, teleportation and more. The range of activities and diversity of spirits would have required an entire company of actors and several closets of costumes and props. I found no indication whatsoever of foul play.

On the night of my induction, a spirit approached me, shyly at first, floating around the periphery of my body, then closer and closer, as if reality itself had dissolved.

*

11/2/1939

Lara,

This has gone entirely too far.

The paper sent you to Vermont as a kind of joke. Of course the twins are a hoax. Your assignment was to write an exposé. I have yet to see any of your purported "legit evidence," unless you count three blurry photographs and one crusty newspaper clipping. You expect us to publish that horseshit? "Disembodied hands appeared, caressed the guests' heads and necks." Aw, Billie, you're going soft.

Look, you don't have to write the article. Never did. Remember it was *your mistake* that landed you at *The Bullet*. We had to print a retraction. I hired you straight out the gate. No experience. You did not know how to ask a single decent question, much less elicit a confession. I taught you everything I know. We put you on the front page.

I admit it was unkind to send you. And I admit that your last six letters were especially disturbing and prompted this response. I do apologize for sending you to the Inn, and I assume some guilt, but NO, you cannot extend your stay. NO, I will not increase your travel funds. In fact, if you so much as set foot in the state of Vermont, you will lose your position, and Lara, we have offered you a very good position. As you know, the paper (and yours truly) were very patient the last time something of this sort occurred; we gave you space, we gave you PAID vacation to clear your head. We are NOT willing to do the same in this case.

R.J. Hammonds

*

11/4/1939

Back in the city Lara does not sleep. Wakes late, walks fifty-six blocks, trying to feel tired again. Smog along the horizon thick as a nail clipping. Traffic in blitzes. Can it be said she misses the Inn? The silence, the sleep? How there is no concept of time at Green Mountain. No need to DO or make use, certainly not think through.

When Horatio told Lara the story of his and William's childhood, he showed no emotion as if he knew, that this was a hurt so resolute it needed nothing but the blunt facts to render whatever listener sympathetic. Although she knew Mr. Hammonds would scoff *hogwash,* she still naïvely thought: if she could just write it out, she could make him and the others believe, and if not believe, at least entertain the possibility that such powers, such miraculous beings, could exist, or simply just feel for them.

Mr. Hammonds barks through the receiver *grow up, Lara. You've been tricked. Don't push me on this.* But if the twins' powers proved false, a lifelong elaborate hoax, so what? Is anything pursued with such sincerity a swindle? Could any lie lived so long still be considered a lie? Say Lara dreamed the entire thing. Say she believed, and believed desperately: then it is so. And it is. But such thoughts would not matter at all if she were at the Inn: she would *be* there.

*

Martin Lyles
BCC Properties
Houston, TX

12/5/1939

Dear Lara,

The lease on your apartment has been terminated per the request of your friend Mr. Hammonds. Your possessions have been placed in storage at the paper's offices downtown. You have thirty days to retrieve them.

Although I have been your landlord (and friend) for five years, I do not take your hasty departure personally. You also left your portentous and breathy diary, resting on your soiled, unmade bed where you apparently felt "too feverish to write or think, much less research new assignments." For a minute, please imagine your little white cat crying by the door, her mews growing hoarser and hoarser, four days alone in your abysmal apartment. Every window flung open, ashtrays toppled over, tea leaves clogging the sink. That is—the apartment H. continued to pay for, despite your penchant for showing up in the middle of the night, stockings ripped, unable to unlock the door.

I am sorry that you found your life here so oppressive, so "corseted by calendars" that you had to ferret away in some tourist trap where the staff will surely indulge all your "NO TIME" and "NOTHING MATTERS" whims, each and every "breathless and dizzy" delusion.

Best,
Lyles

Karen Volkman

Bridge

1.

Bridge's absence gave the creek a new aspect.
Uncrossable, irascible. Crosser stems
on the bank with her will and form,
extension. "Phantom of incapacity
which is me." Bright roar of water,
x of indomitability.

2.

The bridge is not an x. It bridges nothing.
The turmoil is only a portion.

3.

Bridge on the grass is brideless.
Tufts of terra like a bloom in air.
Rational slats, a surface's accretion,
slat system. Grass tints it, heliotropic
emanation, sharp, up, or complex
occupation in shiving rain.

4.

Creek's uncrossability, a new beauty.
"It looked like the process of a thinking,
deep run." It became the suffering of form
and mute suggestion. The syllables
were not perennial. They broke and grew.

5.

The blue pants of the crosser were neither sky
nor water. They orient to the body
as form and boundary. The crosser's green shirt
neither grass nor leaf-thought.
Desire to not get wet, another hurt.

6.

"Glamour of limit, where the rocks just slant"
down the bank, in a wet
stratification, and the creek
spills blows and goings
and is omniform leaving, a prime of seem.

7.

High water as a contour of relation
swells, hurls. The creek which was other
but not antipodal, or refusal. "The wish
to touch it with my phenomenal hand"
loves it as material.

8.

The bridge made the force containable.
Bridgeless the crosser sits, and very still.
"My phenomenal body crosses and longs."
Ceaseless body of the audible.

SARAH ROSE ETTER

Love Film

All of the men I've ever loved are in a line at the front of a very large white room. Their bodies and faces and hair range in shape, color and size. There is no pattern to the men.

The phrase *For a time, for a time, for a time* keeps coming, pestering, echoing.

The first shared the same name as my father and smelled like the South. His accent is fluorescent rattlesnakes. Together, we were claws once.

The second chews tobacco, spits it on the floor into a puddle on the tile and glares at me. I have not returned his phone calls in two years. I kept his love letters in a velvet bag and burned them until the smell choked me.

The third has grown a new beard. His voice is so deep that when he says hello, it reverberates through me, shakes my spine, I go slippery still. That has never quit, will never quit.

The fourth carries a wedding band on his right finger. His wife is not on his face. He stares at me like we are worms in the deepest earth, coiling moist at each other.

The man I thought would be the fifth is not here, and so it seems they think I did not love him at all. They think our love was only lust or hate or scotch. Or else he is dead, which is something that makes my eyes ache like old hearts.

"Well, do something," say the voices over a speaker.

I stare at my four true loves and my true four loves stare back. It is hard to look at them all and not think of the ways we've fucked at the same time.

One by one, I think of fond things for each of them. 1. His hand on my ass in the morning. 2. Our bodies in a hotel bed keeping each other. 3. Driving in an old white Camaro. 4. Mouths full of liquor.

Grouped together like that, my ribs become knives and the room is too hot and terrible to breathe right. They want something, my four true loves, and so do the other men, the men with the speakermouths.

"Rolling," the speakermen say.

My second true love steps up. He is still a hot volcano with yellow teeth.

"We're still in fucking love, you know," he says.

I shake my head but before I can answer him, my first true love steps forward, shoulder-shoving my second true love.

"How did I ever love you if you could love this asshole?" he drawls, Mississippi heat coming from his mouth.

"Good, good," murmur the speakermen.

My married true love glares at me and my other true loves with such hate that it hurts.

"Look at these garbagemen," he says. His disgust is so deep it becomes another person in the room. I have never felt I've disappointed someone so much.

My organs buzz like dying bees, begin to generate vomit.

My third true love stands in the back, shaking his head, staring at his hands as if they are dead birds.

A sense of terribleness rises up in me. I think *For a time, for a time, for a time.* I think *Calm, calm, calm.*

Three of my true loves move toward me. My third true love stays still, stays with his hands.

"Finally," murmurs a speakerman.

The knives come from the back pockets. Some vague men must have supplied them. The three knives are the same in size, the same in silver.

Up against the wall, the plaster feels like all of their hands on my back and ass and neck. The three of them up close become a mosaic, shards of old adoration, terror, sweat.

The married love moves first, was always deft at surgery. His eyes are hateful enough to hold me still, a new kind of anesthetic. I am useless against it.

He and his knife choose my clavicle. He draws a deep line along my collar, slides into me almost gently.

The pain is so clear it becomes yearning. His second line is beneath the first, and he peels back my skin.

He wrenches the bone from me and the sound of the crack sends my head spiraling. My other two loves hold me up.

"Bingo," the speakermen call.

My first love goes second. He is no longer a gentleman.

He chooses my left ear, pushing my head to the side with his knifehand. Everything is too blurred to fight. He whittles at my skin carefully, sawing at the canal to separate me from his prize.

"Mine now," my first love drawls. My eyes are too full of black and white shimmerpain to see what's next.

Then everything stops for a moment.

I am still at the front of the room, minus a bone and an ear.

"Third love," the speakermen buzz. "Third love, you're up!"

My third love stays at the back of the room, staring at me, maybe memorizing all of my blood and the shapes it makes on my skin. My third love has a knife. He must.

"THIRD LOVE," the speakermen bellow. "You, with the shitty beard."

My third love stares into my eyes. Every piece of my heart is already shattered. I thought I was coming here for coffee. Instead, all this skin is slit open and now the third one.

The room is so silent that I can hear my blood shrieking, can hear it leaving various parts of my body while yelling.

Everyone is waiting.

My third love uses his low voice.

"No," he says.

My other loves go still, watching us. Someone has to move, don't they? I keep my eyes trained on my third love. He shakes his head.

"Then no paycheck," the speakermen roar.

The room comes crashing back to life and my second love moves, is a blur before me.

"I have always wanted something to keep," he says, tobacco-breathed.

The pain has become a nail, a needle, a crutch. The remaining loves hold my elbows, make me stay standing.

My second love moves the knife to my lips. I knew he would be cruelest.

He starts below the lip line, scalpeling through the flesh. My knees give out three times, but my other loves hold me steady.

As he knifes around my mouth, my second love hushes: *Mine.*

When my loves let go of my elbows, I pile to the floor. The blood has made me slippery, pain has made me dumb.

I look up a last time. At the edges, my vision has gone white and my loves slide pieces of me into their pockets.

"That's usable footage," a speakerman says. The voice shakes through the walls, down to the bones I have left.

All of my loves leave, the third one still staring at his hands, going home without a thing, never touching me again.

, an in fferent   all too quickly passing   —

the   scenes depict
scenes with all that dwells in the smoke

always the
same—and always a new—   , always the smoke
<?>   the   th ott   the   absent-
minded

could
play   with their backs to the chessboard. It was enough for them to hear the
name   at each turn to be assured of winning.

, a t   present
at the time of the   The end of the
century

e lexi   cal style
succeeded by the systematic and   . . . . The
echoes   ; the   copie   ;
Madel ine   change,   so
many re -Rom e
p.   Interior

The First   copied the   arches and mo ments of   classi-
c   cen   s. Then there was an attempt to re   reinvent more remote
models: the
epoch of

of modern life, always fiery and turbulent, a panorama of gaiety and tears
passing before us like the dust of the   windows

one must invi   in T
. Time spills from   every pore.—   tore m as
the flâneur   who waits.   takes
in the time and renders   expectation.

This recently   posited im tone—   —readily crum-
bles into a dust which,   , is very painful to the eyes

exhumed with   a brush, if not a pickaxe

The introduction of the   system   gave rise to
                    shows the   risi n   dust
                    the inscription: recognition   Mac   from
                          Others represent   ians
                                                    . *Exposition
de la Bibliothèque*

. . . . Between   lies an abyss. But how much
wider the abyss between the dandy and   *Dictionnaire
universelle*
)».

Claretie speaks of a crystal canopy

With reference   We are haunted by what   perhaps
remains   escaped
          turned to   riddle
          li ing in the midst
                                                    , The first
flâneur among the

The wor d in which one is bored—"So what if one is bored! What   fluence can it
possibl   ?" "What   fluence! . . . What   fluence, boredom, with u ? But an
 normous   fluence, . . . a cisive fluence!   ennui, you see, the
    horror verging   veneration. Ennui,   s eyes,
       cu t llowing   the rip of boredom

    let offer a description, full of   , of the condition
of the first pecialized fact   or
boredom in the   weav   : *Ever, ever, ever,* is the
word   from the auto   ment which shakes
    . One can   get used to it. Often the   marks   let
       reverie and the rhythms   occupat)

rainy weather,

sets one dreaming   . Rain makes
everything more hidden,   not only gray but uniform.
until   one can do the same thing—.

                                around the day
                        , like the great idlers, the waterfront loafers
and the vagabonds

                a semblance of consistency.

                            . Particularly

            ... transparent,   when you held it up to the light, all
            illuminated with the very same glow that came from   full   n
    e s .

            a certain unity   the category
of the tedious—in fact, the   tedious of the tedious,   emphatic and
    aligned. *Line up! Eyes*   see
                        ntities of
        tedious.   things,   ; they too are tedious. /
These great   , these great   , these great   , these great   , their
    gnomy .
indicative of unexpected and irregular   edium.

                    a ing of   Exchange, a multi   aire
        he c u t   room
occupied in   English   ascended
case   , and countered   the ve bul major-
domo with white   . He led me into a large glass-roofed
gallery
Something like   boredom   in the air
    as of opium.   between   rows of perches
            various   tries were roosting.
            ; but all seemed to suffer from   sickness. At the extreme end
of the gallery stood a small able   posite a   place, for   this

partly here and partly there,

is co ined , and

vanishes

, believing itself to be the uni and living

. The verse repeats itself perf —imper-

p h ique

the idea doubles

this very keeping our doubles company on another

. Let us think this thought in its most terrible form:

meaning recu t

s h

u T o P),

associating every

think ot to fall into thinking the very aimless-

ness of the wor d the wor d intentionally *voids* a

goal . . .—

. [ ] . . . . , may not

, *cannot* . . . . Thus— lacks

. Niet ,

), [.]

The wor d . . . lives on itself:

The wor d without goal, un joy circle itself a goal; will

a ring feel good to itself

),

the arabesques of its lining.   the   look bored and gray
within   later wakes and wants

           roke   e to   to
signifi nothing else   in no other way can one deal   —structure   relive,
as the embryo   relives   these spaces
flow   without accent, like the   Flânerie   the rhythmics of
                              tortoises
           mimicking the pace of this creatur

Boredom   ,
                              as a mark   . Ornament
boredom

    the double meaning of   term   s

           as   infrastructure of the ide   a
           . The   endless
   me   anical process   repeated over and over again
       . The burden   rock   ing back on the
worn-out

           an incurable   in the very   sence of the present
                                                haps,
                                            its innermost recesses,
and it s

              faces evinced the   traces
           in general

    form   the op t
       display such   faces
              . . . . Moreover, in no other   so much as in this   ,
                                       , is the   bearable boredom
so   ment .
       silence and reserve,
would most certainly be the exception.

BRANDON SHIMODA

Blessèd Handsome One

I sit in——grass————weak
My feet are ugly————bends, but do not finish
Ass——disappoint
Bent—flaking my spine
With warm sun moves, keeps up with
It—continues
In the shade of original prison

We will soon be moving, but never act, no,
Sit in grass, lacking desire—wind
Gives connectors a break
The sun is 93000000 miles. How do I set one on me?
I am in a majestic——one
Will never know the sun
To know is the killing of—kills what it is that is known

Shut up—don't question
Dumb—light
Reconciling intelligence——intelligence, understand————being
Sympathetic————the sun is
93000000 from where I am, and oh
Blessèd handsome one, you will just have
To take the tar well

Good Fortune Blow Island

Twin moons straighten a perfume
A single night dances
Evening
Many...
Chronic Many
Moons in crystal rigging
Fashioned in silent orbits RESCUE
Making certain the locals are not vindictive
Before...
The challenging feet
Soft pastimes can alleviate
A network of nations
Over entire bodies
Luminous Replacing thought
GELID PANTOMIME I am
Mother I am waiting for my husband
To recognize me
In the light of the funeral

Midnight flames after
We are walking away Throwing circles from sockets
Skulls' affections To be sure Circles in celebratory fonts
Will a stranger deliver me?
From the third moon Collaborative
Between two establishments
When establishments
Crumble
Erections?
I did not get the signal I was studying the blue tarp
Protecting the hole in the earth
From celestial fallout
The season was entering manifestations of the season
The tarp was distraction I knew mistakes were imminent

Energy becomes substance on earth
A flaw
Devours soap
Expands the centrifuge of the flaw
Grows dizzy
Labia as it likes
A new township in which moons are God
Third being the thumb Two people looking in the same direction
Two people appearing to be looking in the same direction
Crafts in the harbor What instantaneous thought
The mother did not teach but had three sons
Wanting her husband
Standing over a rice cracker LUNAR
End of that moment
DIERESIS
Going into the street for a few minutes just a few
To catch something Touch statues
Influence VINEGAR POEM
Going down on the field
To inhale Act 2
Before it begins

I wanted to be someone wear my shirt inside-out
I was afraid I was afraid Where does the scalp end?
I was going by color and title
Not that the world was small The world was large
A snake coiled in the healer's leg
Never turns upon itself
As soon as it is alone
Amounts to years of unaddressed pain
A rock I would like to sit...

THERE IS NO FUTURE THE EMPTY TOMB
Waiting arrival Lowering hands into a basin
Of fat—to the arm
Cannot stop I did not linger like
Elements creeping out of tar Sky protruding a vast fortress
Infection People growing hopeless
Slapping flags on a fair game Winch
Hanging from a tree
I voted for a value for a thing that did not exist
Picked up and bolted
The branch Put
Screws to anyone
Who spent more time in juice Less
Scared into revolutionary lands wanting movement
Between Not because
One's influences are committed to being mindful
There is no money in that Flung upon a pack animal
Conveyed to the reunion
In time to see the squad
Become astral
Earth Peacock in a crack
On the side of a vase
Neither the content nor the content's protection
TIMELESS MEDIUM

Any death is only an interruption
Poetry is the abandonment of "Completion"
—Ryuichi Tamura, "Water"
Becomes architectural Proposes a solution to the problem
The loquat strikes up Moves outward
The pool…
The roof
Friends in dark ruins with them
Total and Beauty Closing over a leek
BIAS OF SHADOW

Returning that made the arrival
Visible
Mastery
Underfeeding emptiness

One could taste radiation soaring
Open hearts Agents of prayer
Reading all the way to the afterlife there

The Black Corner

To the woman revealing herself
As the opposite of change—the legs of a fragmentary brother
Will grow crossed from your stomach—

To be inherent is a beautiful script
Every day parts the script growing only what is already eating
Organs
Eviscerated
Before a captivated crew
Doing nothing thereafter Not crying
Not fishing among folds in their laps
For a way to call forth emotion simply waxen

A river flows
Under a frozen river
The woman is not looking for anything not attempting anything
Does not feel compelled to write down anything now

A stranger casually suggested to me, *This woman could be the kind of
woman who could walk just as easily upside down as right side up. This could be
the fording of a new and circular space*

To which I asked, *Because why? Because…legs are growing out of her
stomach? A brother bears self-motivation, and the lust, even a simple desire, to
go where he likes, where fear is the warmest.* To which I then added, *Where
would she walk even if she could? The world is just as traditional either way, as
challenged to remain tending brains for trod hemorrhage*

Every day must be felt on the finger
Popular violence walking with hands before us feeling along the script
Blinding a hole into everything
Every character ruling the earth Every body of translucent skin
Torn

Into a swath
As a cape Wailing bulb
Pulled loose from a throat that makes peace with the ground
Revolving the hateful and unyielding cube
To get to the black corner
Where affections are laid
And especially if poorly

Lips
Torn from the faces of people
With no wiser experiment
In life
Or reverse over metamorphic earth
Remain as relics of a dense and delinquent care
An oval of lava and silver claws

Joy Wood

Gap Year

Summer

My boyfriend broke up with me by pushing me out of a moving car. I didn't even have time to think before I hit pavement. The skin on my legs came off all bunched up like ribbon candy. My teeth knocked together, my tongue in the way, the sound trapped in my head. His car kept going.

When I found myself again I was fetal. Surprised more than anything else, my bones shimmering with insult from the fall. In the distance, I could see the interstate, cars and trucks and RVs headed north, where there were casinos and giant burritos to be had, drivers speeding towards billboard promises.

This was how it had started: he had loved me, and then he didn't.

He'd said, "This has gone as far as it can go."

"This? You mean us?" I asked.

He didn't say anything, just turned a dial. Blue fluid spat onto the windshield. Two off-kilter rainbows opened up in the dust and bugs. He reached across my lap to open the door.

I sat on the side of the road, knees bent, palms propping myself up, as though warming myself by a fire. Something clear oozed down my shins.

A station wagon stopped. Inside were a man and a woman, both wearing floppy canvas hats and sunglasses on nylon cords. "Are you okay?" the woman asked. It was always the woman who asked these kinds of questions. The man flexed his fingers, then re-gripped the wheel. Classical music leaked from the open window.

I nodded.

"Can we take you somewhere?"

I told them where I lived.

"What's your name?" the woman asked.

"Michelle," I said, which was a lie. "My roommate's at home," which was another lie because I lived alone.

Through the window, I watched fast food signs mark the way back to the city. The tall hat of Arby's signaled we were getting close. I flexed my toes inside my sneakers, preparing for when I would have to stand. It could have been worse.

At the entrance to my apartment complex, I said, "Here is fine."

"Dan can bring you to your door," the woman said. "It's no trouble."

"That's really not necessary," I said. "Thank you for the ride."

The woman fumbled in her purse, then pressed a business card into my palm. "Let me know if there's anything we can do."

I ran my fingers over the embossed letters as I walked to my door. They waited for me to go inside. The keys in my pocket felt distant and irretrievable, like a bell sewn into a dog toy. I let myself in, flicked my porch light twice so they'd know I'd gotten in safely, and went to bed.

I stayed there for two days. My bedroom had windows on three sides and I watched my mattress make a sundial on the floor. My wounds stuck to the sheets, left stains.

On the third day, he called. "Do you want your stuff?"

He had nothing of mine that I could possibly want.

Milk formed skin over a cereal bowl I'd left in the sink. My knees looked like topographic maps. It was ninety degrees outside and I had to wear pants when I went out in public. At night, I checked the progress of my legs. I kept hydrogen peroxide, cotton balls, and Neosporin on the coffee table. The bright voices on TV kept me company as I peeled off the bandages. Baths were bad for healing but I took them anyway, leaned back and let the water lift my legs up.

I'd moved to New Mexico a year earlier to take a job in development for an environmental nonprofit. My boss Bridget had fled New York, but acted as though she still lived in the city. When she told people—cashiers, caterers, reporters—what she needed from them, they responded by blinking rapidly. It was my job to smooth the path between Bridget and our donors. Some of them were only two or three years older than I was, rich from oil and natural gas, their skinny necks swaddled in expensive ties, called me "sweetie" or "darling." It made me want to kick them in the throat. Instead, I made snowflakes out of paperclips and took home toilet paper in my purse. I met my boyfriend through work. He was a reporter for a weekly newspaper, and would file stories in his boxers a minute before deadline. I enjoyed being the responsible one, who let him hit the snooze button while I got up to pack my lunch. We'd been together for over a year.

I declined invitations from friends who worked downtown. I didn't know how to tell them what had happened over happy hour margaritas.

Route 66 ran through the center of the city, and motels lined both sides of the avenue. Every Friday night, I would get dinner from a drive-through and check into one because it was easier to sleep alone in a bed that wasn't mine. I took a shower using the free toiletries. When I was finished, my skin and hair felt drier than before. I flipped through the Bible and phone book to see what had been dog-eared by previous guests. Inside the nightstand, someone had written *Veronica* in blue Sharpie.

In the mornings, I ate waffles and watched children throw Cheerios at their siblings while their parents argued over road atlases. Labor Day weekend I saw a kayak slide off the roof of a Jeep leaving the motel's parking lot. A pickup truck hit the kayak. Yellow fiberglass filled the avenue like pencil shavings.

Fall

Birthmarks run in my family, but skipped me. My cousin has a raised one over her right collarbone. Men she dated were always asking about it, then would kiss it as though they were out to prove something. "At first they think it's a scar," she said. "When I tell them what it really is they lose interest."

My scabs itched. "That's how you know they're healing," she said. She told me to rub vitamin E oil on them. It reminded me of using Pledge to polish my grandmother's dining room table.

I missed the trees back east in Massachusetts, the sound of leaves under my feet, how I could spend entire afternoons raking my lawn, pulling a path through the grass. My apartment was across the street from the public high school, and sometimes I could hear the marching band practice, the brass filling my head. Two doors down, a fat man had a pomeranian, and I would watch him walk it after work, both of them shuffling down the sidewalk on their short legs.

Around the neighborhood, kiddie pools were being thrown out, deflated and left on curbs like abandoned spacecraft. My ex-boyfriend's contact lens solution sat in my medicine cabinet. There was no possible scenario in which he would show up on my doorstep urgently needing to wash his eyes.

This low-slung city was not big enough for both of us. I went to get ice cream in Nob Hill and saw him trying to parallel park through the window of the parlor, his arm gripping the passenger headrest. My thumb went though my waffle cone and I had to press my mouth to the leak.

I started volunteering at a day care inside a shelter for women who had experienced domestic abuse. The day care was in the basement of the shelter for reasons I didn't like to think about. Visitors had to be buzzed in through two sets of locked doors. Even though the staffers always left in pairs for safety, some of the mothers carried purses that cost more than my rent. The mothers didn't look like their Lifetime-movie counterparts. No black eyes or Frankenstein stitches. They spoke in complete sentences. They wiped snot from the faces of their sons and daughters, their own brows unmoving. I wondered what their stories were.

I could hide my own. I put on pants and to the world I looked okay, but every time one of the kids drove a remote-control truck into my shins, I had to keep from screaming. My bandages crinkled when I crossed my legs. The treasure of the playroom was a large pink dollhouse that hinged open. Kids loved to suck on the corners of the scalloped roof.

A boy named Hugo was my favorite. He was five, and his hair was buzzed on the sides and long on top, which made him look like he was growing a thought. When someone wouldn't share with him or sat in the chair he liked, he'd say, "Don't be a fool."

One afternoon four girls were playing with the dollhouse. Hugo went over, put two Barbies and a Ken inside, then shut the halves. "They're shaking things up inside," he said.

I didn't ask him to repeat himself, or what he meant.

On Tuesdays and Thursdays, a counselor came to meet with the children. Linda, the director of the shelter, and Penelope, her assistant, would wipe everything down with disinfectant in preparation for her visits, including the laminated posters upstairs with titles like *Core Beliefs* and *The Cycle of Abuse,* as if all problems could be solved by geometry.

The counselor's name was Bonnie and she brought art supplies with her, plastic clay and watercolor paints where the yellow had darkened like the yolk of a hard-boiled egg. After Bonnie was finished with her sessions, I offered her a cup of grape juice. I never asked her what she talked about with them.

I always felt guilty when I left the shelter because I could leave alone after Penelope had walked me to my car. I could drive back to my empty apartment where no one was waiting to hurt me. What happened to me could have been worse. I had no trouble filling in the details of what didn't happen. He could have punched me in the stomach. He could have broken my nose. He could have pushed me out on the highway, where I might not have survived the impact. Before I turned the key in the ignition, I checked the rearview mirror. Only me.

When I got home from the shelter, I would turn on the TV and watch people fix things or cook things or guess the prices of things.

I had to go to a benefit dinner for work, so I went to the salon for the first time in months. The hairdresser combed my wet bangs over my face. The scissors were cold on my cheeks. I started to cry.

Winter
Albuquerque had over 300 sunny days per year. My legs had healed, the scars like fish-net stockings I couldn't take off.

Things were slow at work. Donors were off skiing in Taos, in Aspen. I arranged the holiday cards sent to the office in alphabetical order. At the shelter, I watched Hugo do his homework, tracing letters and words to learn their shapes.

On the advice of others, I bought a journal. I bought a fishbowl.

The ruled lines went unfilled. I put mail in the fishbowl. I was afraid to start something again. Pencil, pen, paint, crime scene re-enactments that I was watching too much of on TV—sooner or later I got back to the same place. You never see a dust bunny or hairball form: they just appear.

The last time I saw Hugo, two days before Christmas, he told me that he was moving to Texas. "I'm going to be a cowboy," he said.

Hugo's mother stroked his head and smiled. Her front teeth were pigeon-toed. "We're going to be closer to family."

"I got you a present," Hugo said. "Close your eyes."

I held out my hands.

He had given me three crayon stubs, the paper wrapping frayed.

"Thank you," I said.

"It's nothing," he said.

Spring

I checked into a motel for my birthday. I told myself it would be the last time. The ice machine grumbled with effort as it filled my bucket. I opened a bottle of whiskey that I'd bought at a liquor store down the street. I saved the ice for myself, let it melt in my fist as I drank because it felt good and hurt at the same time.

There was a new girl at the shelter. Maria had braces and sneakers that lit up as she walked. She was from Rio Rancho. Her father was a surgeon. Maria's mother, Dee, wore bug-eye sunglasses and had fingernails as shiny as jellybeans. Maria ate apples with two hands, her hair getting sticky in the process.

"How old are you?" she asked me.

"How old do you think I am?" I said.

She squinted. "Fifteen."

I laughed. That was how old I was when I found my first gray hair.

For Mother's Day, I sent my mother an arrangement of bloodless flowers, pinks and lavenders and yellows. I called her to see if she'd received them. She'd just come back from brunch with my aunt and cousin. At the end of the call, I told her that I loved her.

"I love you, too," she said, and laughed. "You know what the best response is? 'I love you more.'"

I finally told someone. I couldn't see her face, which made it easier to begin.

The second and third were quicker than the first. Our mutual friends blamed the past, the situation. *Oh, he didn't mean it. He didn't have good role models growing up. His father used a belt on him.* At home, I tore open leftover ketchup packets and chewed on the crimped ends.

You shouldn't take it personally.

I got a promotion at work. My boss took me out to lunch and gave me a cupcake with CONGRATULATIONS! on it, the word squeezed across the top.

Friday night, Dee was late picking up Maria. Penelope, who'd offered to stay and wait with me, was re-doing her makeup, drawing the lines thicker. "You got plans tonight?" she asked.

"No," I said, because it was easier than lying.

Penelope sprayed perfume in the air, then walked through the cloud.

"I want to go home," Maria said. She'd stopped drawing and was pressing the tip of her marker into the paper.

Through the security camera feed I watched Dee park her Mercedes across two spaces. "Maria, let's get your backpack."

Penelope and I led Maria upstairs to meet her mother. Dee was dressed like she was going to a job interview. She hugged Maria, then covered her ears.

"I just told her father I wanted a divorce," Dee said. Her eyes gleamed. "We had irreconcilable differences. I wanted to live."

I looked at the round chrome bell on the sign-in counter. I wanted to ring it, keep ringing it, the sound spreading under my fingers until it was the only thing in my head, the striking made clean.

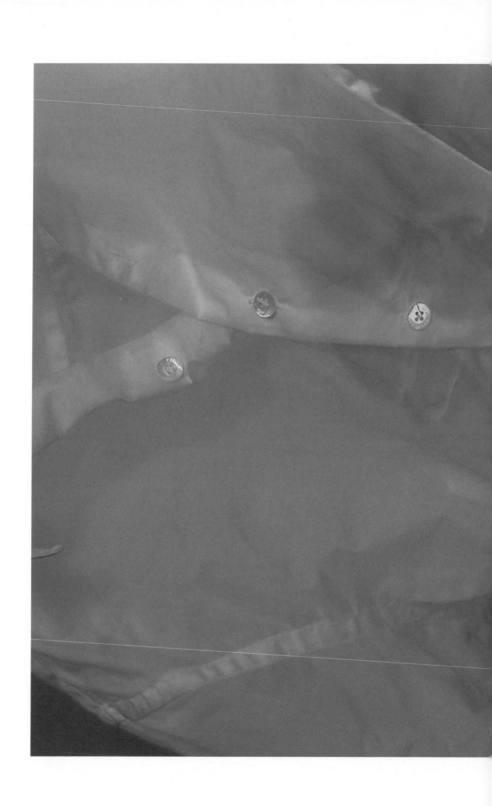

I. LIQUID GROUND 2
2011, 160 x 110 in.

II. LIQUID GROUND 2
2011, 160 x 110 in.

III. LIQUID GROUND 3
2011, 160 x 110 in.

IV. LIQUID GROUND 4
2011, 160 x 110 in.

V. LIQUID GROUND 5
2011, 160 x 110 in.

VI. LIQUID GROUND 6
2011, 160 x 110 in.

Dan George

Tea with Ms. Quan

soft edges ripening in the sun of an empty bag

*

I've been thirsting for the future textures
this pumpkin decomposing articulates our atmosphere

Let's manifest a line the mind finds charming
sexual ripened ethereal

Black grapes ripening in the hill's white hands?
animal transforming into night

Autumn rolled through the trees shaking his fist of coins—
red is the dress of the leaves as they open

FARID MATUK

New Romantics

Carry carrier the disease
is not a bad thing is forever
new romantics sing precise
of them women inside me

cherry wine Faye had butt
kids dance close without touching
fall into your comfort, grain
dance quinoa purple
pink orange yellow sun

wave up the hill and back
up dancers raise their stockinged knees
to the left describe the world
our grown heads against the glass

a herpes flowers at the corner
of our mouths' mouth
we are beautiful, it's gonna be a beautiful night.

To the moon full face we are turning
away Saint Sebastian displayed the moon
petrifies. I want us to put on our coyote skin
go loping snout-free
fuzz out the night, the Pacific
and go louder every tree is a channel
I want to talk in eucalyptus skins peel
line the road eucalyptus oil something something wildfire.

Great whites make love outside and salt blows back
an orange is feeding my daughter in Virginia
she reached up you said peppermint
tea fog against your ribs
against the door you hung
you're so possible, long feet
walking a new constellation down the city
piss, run to catch up.

The fog turns away the night, let the night turn away from the moon
let the moon turn away so I can see it
I want to burrow in the hot, hot sand, I want to know everything
I want to eat your ass, to seep into our next selves
tender love, lots of babies, the sign for more.

Christina Manweller

Body :: Water :: Flight :: (Fading)

All in one day, the day we see a coyote standing stock still in the street outside our house, my husband tells me:

1. A man drowned in waist deep water at a beach near San Francisco while seventy people watched from shore.

2. Elsewhere, a firefighter lost his job for saving someone using a method he wasn't trained in.

3. His cousin is worse, her brother and father beside themselves because they can't help her, she is steadily deteriorating.

4. An elderly couple survived a tornado by stowing away in their bathtub. The twister ripped through the house lifting the tub and dropping it a hundred feet off, the two still inside it. Survivors of a tornadic tempest in another state sat in their broken house talking to an interviewer. The kettle stood on the same burner it was on in the pre-tornado instant.

I tell him: Like in the Big Thompson flood when a house was sheared in half but the glasses stood just so in the cupboard as if nothing had happened.

Yeah, he says, like that.

My husband exaggerates, so I expect some of these stories are stretched. I look up the one about the man drowning and find that, in fact, seventy-five people watched him die, including City of Alameda firefighters and police (though the water was neck deep, not waist deep). Now I see that #2 makes #1 seem doubly

so from what I've been reading, it seems possible
that time is merely a mental construct, that
although it appears to us a landscape

tragic. Doubly tragic.

solid as the one we're moving through, it may not
even exist. There are people in the world—the
Hadza in Tanzania, Moken sea gypsies in Thailand,
the Amondawa in Brazil—not operating within
the same time-constricted universe we are.
Perhaps they seem backward from a certain
techno-centric standpoint but to me they are to
be envied. They don't

Concerning #1, the drowning man: Rescue personnel ended up watching
from the beach against all human instinct because they lacked necessary
resources and training, reportedly on account of budget cuts. They were
doing as they'd been told.

The concluding minutes of his life were spent all alone in the company of
seventy-five observers. (What did he think, everyone staring from shore,
nobody coming to the rescue? Did he have second thoughts? Did he say to
himself, I must finish what I've started, people are watching? Did he say,
Surely one of them will come?)

We humans are rule-following creatures. I am

worry like we do. They don't obsess over the future,
or about all they haven't done—no bucket list!—
or about age. If time is a mental construct, then
we're not all

obedient. It runs in my German genes. Also, self-protective. I wonder

looking at the same picture.

what I would've done on that beach. I hate to think.

Es ist verboten!

The concept of time inside my husband's head is vastly different from mine, as if we live in separate realities. Our movements, even, reflect this. I'm quick, both in action and reaction, while he is much slower; we frustrate one another, coexisting at our different tempos.

Excerpted from the City of Alameda police department dispatch (mistypes appear in the original):

11:31:53 "RP SAYS HER FRIENDS SON ZACK, RAYMOND WM-55 IS MENTALLY ILL AND IS GOING TO FAR OUT IN THE WATER. RP FEELS HES TRYING TO KILL HIMSELF"
11:32:11 "OP IS WEARING ALL BLK SHIRT AND BLU JEANS"
11:33:11 "ON PHONE WITH MOTHER . . ."

I'm thinking of my great-great-grandfather, whose picture stands on a table in the hall. He was a house painter, bicycle racer, captain of the fire department. It's hard to get my mind around him being born in 1865; he seems like someone you'd see on the street today, just a regular Joe looking a tad awkward in a suit. Actually, he's inordinately handsome. He must have gone to a second-rate photo studio because the arm of the chair he's sitting in is well worn where previous sitters rested their arms. Of course, Fullerton, Nebraska, probably didn't have a plethora of studios to choose from in the late 1800s.

The day before his thirty-eighth birthday, he was ferrying neighbors across the spring-melt bloated Loup River. Returning from the final trip he'd nearly reached shore when the boat flipped. He managed to climb on top—or rather, on bottom—was carried about a quarter-mile downstream before slamming into wood from the washed out bridge which knocked him into the wild rushing water. Men onshore put out a boat and threw a rope. He missed it.

The body wasn't found for months. He left Grace, his thirty-one-year-old widow, and five kids to grow up as he did, fatherless.

> Our Sudanese friends joke sometimes about
> our differing notions of time. If we agree to meet
> at a particular hour they laugh and ask, African
> time or your time? They know how to ease,
> how to let go in a way I can't seem to learn.
> Teach me?

A friend from Nebraska describes the Loup (*loup*: French for "wolf") as fluctuating between modest stream and mile-wide marvel, quadrupling in width in places—practically a sea. At Fullerton, it's fast and narrow.

On that early spring day, the river lived up to its name.

When I describe my great-great-grandfather's ordeal to another friend, she says, That river was *trying* to kill him.

> Intriguing that the Amondawa of Brazil don't
> count years, they mark milestones by changing
> their names. For instance, a child will give her
> name to a newborn and take on a new one. This
> makes perfect sense. We all know of people who
> were given a name that suited them at one time
> but seemed to grow flat or just plain wrong as they
> got older (reminding me of the dog I named Buddy

who was terrified of people and not buddy-like at
all). It seems unfortunate, the way a name doesn't
always suit one.

More than twenty years after his father drowned, Guy, oldest son of
the Loup's victim, pulled a drowning man from an eastern Colorado
reservoir. A reverse karma sort of thing. Perhaps his father's death made
him ultra sensitive to water's menace, its natural antagonism to the human
life-form.

Beware.

Sometimes we can't save ourselves. Sometimes nobody saves us.

A clock has no significance

Ask my husband's cousin, stricken by a desert disease called
coccidioidomycosis, a.k.a. Valley Fever, picked up when she lived in
Arizona. It took a long time to diagnose because the symptoms point to
more common ailments including flu and lung cancer. Now she lives with
a declining body and little hope for a cure. The fungus-spawned disease
attacks the lungs, moving on in rare cases—in her case—to other organs.
Her husband left her when she fell ill so she lives by herself in a nursing
home.

to the Hadza of Tanzania who sleep when they're tired,
whether day or night. I, on the other hand, am tied
to the timekeeper. I eat and sleep at the same hours
every day. Though I am in bed punctually every
night, I feel unrested mornings, even when I've
spent the allotted time sleeping. My dreams are
busy and stress filled; I wake exhausted, as if I've
been living too many lives.

Sometimes we can't save ourselves. Sometimes nobody saves us. Ask

Guy's son, my grandfather, killed by a mysterious ailment. Ask me,

> Living clockless, calendarless: I can't imagine. I am
> curious about their dreams, these people

sometime in the future.

    11:35:20 "USCG ADVISED, 40 MIN ETA"
    11:36:05 "HAVE VISUAL ABOUT 150 YRD OUT"
    11:36:30 "CONTACT WITH ACSO ASCERTAIN IN THEIR BOAT IS OUT"
    11:36:56 "ACSO HAS NO BOAT OUT TODAY"
    11:37:59 "ACRECC STATES ALAMEDA DOESN'T HAVE A BOAT"

On July 31, 1976, coinciding with Coloradans' celebration of the state's centennial, a flash-storm sent a nineteen foot wall of water bellowing down canyon below Rocky Mountain National Park, hurling great conifers and boulders the size of bulldozers, lifting RVs and cars into its mad course where they bobbed like plastic colored beads. When a Coke machine bounced past the motel window, a couple on vacation fled up the mountain. Propane tanks barreled down the Big Thompson river exploding as they went. Survivors perched on the mountainside later told of cars sweeping by below, some blaring their horns, some not, passengers waving flashlights in frantic S.O.S's. A family plowing their way down-canyon at the last minute passed a girl standing on the road, waist deep in water, hands on her face, screaming...

> living outside time.

screaming...

> All those existences we dive into while asleep! Time
> unrolling so that we can be in thousands—

millions?—more places, interacting with people we've never met. Who are they? Where do they come from? In the morning I often remember three to five dreams, one has cut into the next and then that one was broken too—one after another after another—and then I wake, breaking the chain again. What if it's the dreamlife that is most real? Sometimes it is.

A Pete Seeger anthem rushes my mind "…we were waist deep in the Big Muddy…waist deep in the Big Muddy…and the big fool said to push on …the big fool said to push on."

Pushing on, or not pushing on, we so often make the wrong decisions. Too often, it's not obvious how wrong until later. I will have just one more drink. We will wait for someone else to take the initiative.

My daughter hates the sound of a clock ticking. One summer when visiting my parents she took all the clocks in our room—why so many?—and carried them to the bathroom, shutting them in to tick tick tick together, unheard. Take that!

I think about the girl on the roadside. Perhaps if my mind weren't quite so visual, I wouldn't keep picturing a person I've never seen. I want to weep for her but I don't, I'm dry as a desert rock. She feels far away, as if she never existed. I can't help feeling, though, that I should love her, this terrified girl whose life may have ended that summer day all those years ago when I was a kid. Why don't I? Is it impossible to love

A dream can break distinctly into our daily life, even years later. For instance: Einstein's famous cow dream leading finally to the strange idea that time is relative. I don't have dreams that are prescient or even all that useful to me. I dream of houses. I've lived in more houses in dreamtime than the richest kings ever owned. Small ones, big ones, right ones, wrong ones. Houses with secret rooms, or with people living there already, unseen. Houses with fatal flaws, like the beautiful seaside home rushed by water when the tide came in. What do the house dreams say about me? I suspect they're a sign of never quite being satisfied. I'm searching...searching...

those we've never encountered directly?

12:06:20 "LOST SITE CONTACT COAST GUARD"
12:08:04 "[CITIZEN] CALLING FROM [REDACTED TEXT] SHORELINE DR [REDACTED TEXT] SAYS HE CAN SEE MALE FLOATING
12:08:41 "USCG ADVISED . . . ONE OF THE COAST GUARD OFFICERS DID HAVE INTERMITTENT VISUAL ON THE OP. UNK IF AT THIS TIME . .
THERE IS A SMALL BOAT AND A HELICOPTER ENRT"
12:08:53 "RP SAYS ITS A WM RED HAIR EARLY 50'S"

This morning I was dreaming that I walked through a large square building of many stories— no, not a house for once. People moved about doing this and that, active in the crowded space.

My husband and I flee to the mountains for a weekend; we're staying at a friend's place. The lodgepole pines here have been attacked en bloc by the mountain pine beetle (*Dendroctonus ponderosae*)—a scourge no bigger in length than the word DEAD and only slightly plumper—turning the forested mountainsides into patches of brown where the stricken pines stand, interspersed with green splotches where aspen groves thrive. (I was once told that lodgepoles are a preferred tree for teepee-building because they are so straight

I proceeded through and among them

and tall. They are: tall and shallow-rooted; one has toppled near our friend's house, its air-exposed roots a small tight bundle at odds with the tree's great height.)

Without my glasses on, the far-off terrain still looks attractive, with green smudging nicely into brown creating the illusion of all's-mostly-well.

looking for the way out.

The river here is running frighteningly full because of heavier than usual winter and spring snows. Sandbags line sections of it. My husband says flood warnings have been issued. When we get into bed it's raining so hard I can't sleep for picturing that river rising.

8 am: snow on the ground, though it's June 20th. The river still rushes inside its banks.

I asked someone where the stairs were; she pointed to the back wall. I passed a woman

On the other side of the window, a hummingbird, maybe freshly arrived from Mexico.

Stellula calliope, the calliope hummingbird, is the world's tiniest long distance avian migrator, 5,600 miles round-trip following the Sierra Madre Occidental and the North American Cordillera. It's partial to the high Colorado mountains and should be haunting these parts by now, though I couldn't identify one unless it held still for half a second. All I see here is blur.

sweeping the vast empty space.

The calliope, only member of the genus *Stellula* (little star), is surely the fastest moving heavenly body in all the cosmos.

> Spotting a pendant on the floor, a silver heart, I went to pick it up, realizing then that it was one of several the sweeper had piled. Then once again I was trying to leave the building and discovered I'd lost a small black dog that had been following me. Now a rattling racket inserted itself into my awareness. It was the tree outside the open window, disrupted by a leaping squirrel. I lie still, readjusting to the new world, the "real" world, my lives jumbled à la Proust and his fallen away map, his temporary loss of self—the self he most identified with anyway.

We counted eight baby wood ducks smaller than my fist on the pond near home a few weeks ago. But we've not seen them lately. I suppose the night herons got them like they did last year—we saw one of the neckless Churchill-esque avians not long ago, perching pondside on a grey rock. Grey on grey.

> 12:09:02 "APPEAR TO SEE SOME OF OPS CLOTHING"
> 12:10:01 "NO ANSWER AT COAST GUARD BOAT # GIVEN"
> 12:18:48 "COAST GUARD UNABLE TO MOVE THEIR BOAT INTO THE WATER, TOO SHALLOW . . . USCG CONTACTING OFD FOR MUTUAL AID"
> 12:19:00 "CONTACT EBRPD FOR BOAT"
> 12:20:16 "EBRPD HAS NO BOAT OUT"

A woman took her life at the little neighborhood park a few months back. This is not generally known; a man I trust told me.

> I've dreamed those who've wronged me. Occasionally they come to say how sorry they are,

making me feel clean, lifted up after, as if they'd
really been here, and all is set right. I know these
are only dreams. I know that. But what if our
souls travel at night now and then, risking what
we, in our bodily selves, can't, saying I'm sorry, I
love you. I hope

Wood ducks hatch in treed nests, leaping to the ground or water within a
day of birth from heights up to 300 feet.

my soul has done that.

Did those herons pick off every last one?

For years a mandarin duck, cousin to our American wood duck, lived on
that pond. It was a gorgeous deep-hued bird, flamboyant, with a rich red
beak, pale rust wings tipping gracefully skyward at the rear and a white
swoosh that started in front of the eye and curved over the black upper
back.

I wonder.

We have a photo of him paddling around with a local female. It's a mystery
how that bird ended up here.

In his writings Aristotle mentions the *klepsydra*

A neighbor says: Nature is *violent*. This comes on the heels of another
neighbor telling of watching a fox bury a cat in her garden, coming back
later to dig it up, leaving just the tail behind.

That evening, the fox returned for even the tail, that whip of vertebrae,
cartilage, muscle and tendon.

—literally, water thief—a water clock used in
ancient Greece to keep court proceedings in

hand. The amount of water granted depended on the gravity of the case, more serious trials were allotted more water, that is, more time.

My husband tells me he saw a fox family gamboling on the grass down the street the other day. If you have to feed hungry kits even a tail may be a delicacy. Or else a toy for playing tug-of-war.

What an ordinary violent fecund spring here in Colorado.

We harness up the dog and walk to the lake a mile or so from home. Arriving at a wide stretch of beach, all pebble and rock, we come to what looks like a hunk of wood. The dog pulls hard toward it and I let her until we get close and wood morphs into flesh. It's a fish, stiff and stretched into a U, the tail and head aiming skyward, a bite taken out of its side.

On the lake a skinny cormorant, escapee from the dinosaur epoch, holds its own flashing unwieldy prize. Maneuvering the vertebrate tail-up into a throat long and narrow takes a while. The prey is wider than the passage, is thrashing like a hellion, but at last it goes on down.

Yes, nature is hungry.

Is the clock tick-ticking here in this room a physical manifestation of my mind's fantasy? Our collective fantasy? What time should I be at work? In bed? Tick-tick-tick-

On the way home we go by house after silent house. It's a weekday morning. One tiny cottage with a yard orderly in summer is now surrounded by weeds a foot tall. The dianthus in the small garden is spindly, the flowers pathetic and grass-choked. I notice, though, that the red-trimmed windows stand cranked open. Passing, I smell coffee, notice an old trouble light hanging by the door: an impromptu porchlight, bulb still burning inside its cage though the sun's been up for hours.

At the next house, a woman's face at a window.

tick.

12:20:18 "STILL HAS VISUAL LOOKS LIKE SUBJECT IS
FLOATING"
12:24:40 "EBRPD HAS A SMALL ZODIAK AT TIDWATER
IN OAKLAND THAT CAN RESPOND IF
NEEDED."
12:29:04 "CIVILIAN BRINGING SUB IN"
12:29:52 "CRIME SCENE SCREENS"

I once saw a Dürer exhibit in Vienna. I love his combination of the detailed
and the fanciful (da Vinci meets Blake). In 1512 he painted the wing of a
European roller, a crow-sized bird of brilliant plumage. At the top, where
pinion would join body, a powdery spray in pearl ash blooms; this is the
essential bit, soul of the thing, matter, imbued. He noted each rachis and
barb, flawed and not, as well as placement of curve and variation in hue.
Blue, green, russet. Cream and black. White. Mildest grey. After all of
it, ash is what

> If time is created in the mind, then infinity must
> be another mental construct. Perhaps, though,
> infinitude is the natural state

he returns to.

> of things in a way that we can't comprehend (it
> seems we comprehend so little). The more I learn
> the less

We return to.

> I know.

12:30:48 "SUBJ ON SHORE"
12:31:20 "AFD DOING CPR"
12:36:54 "AFD TRANSPORTING"
12:41:10 "SCREENS NO LONGER NEEDED"
12:56:18 "FINALTYPE: 5150 —> SUICID"

> The ouroboros, symbol for infinity, is not in fact
> infinite; it's incomplete, consisting as it does of a
> beginning—the mouth—and an end

Did Dürer come across his brilliant bird already dead? Or kill it?

> —the tail. The snake holding its tail in its mouth
> creates an illusory perfect circle. Couldn't the
> mouth open at any moment and the tail slip free,
> cutting a hole in infinity? Of course, infinitude
> may be relative.

A while back I found a smallish bird, brown with a brilliant yellow stripe sweeping its tail. It was dead on the balcony, just laid out there, the glistening yellow shouting *yes! yes! spring! spring!* while the stiff still body whispered *no no.*

> I dreamed that my daughter disappeared.
> Literally. As if she never was. I screamed my
> throat raw. Sleeping beside me, my husband woke
> in terror at my terror. Though I've had my share
> of nightmares, this was the worst of my life.

Maybe I would've painted it, were I a painter.

> Hear that—sounds like an ancient wooden flute?

Outside the library, a woman plucks flowers from the big round planter beside the door making a bouquet in one hand; with the other she presses a phone to her ear. Snow-in-summer, marigold, snapdragon—she's pluck-pluck-plucking, talk-talk-talking. I collect my books inside, pass her on the way out, bouquet scattered at her feet, talking, talking.

it's an owl—I hear it every day but have never
seen it—I did find a feather: striped, creamy tan

What I mean to say:

true, sometimes   spilled   love   as

if   bottomless glass.   we   ,
one another. Oh   .   .

Amen.

and brown—see I keep it here on the side table.

17:38:31 "IN DATE: 05-30-11 *TIME: 17: 38* . . .
NAME: ZACK RAYMOND PAUL* MAIL
ADDR AS OF 10-20-10: [REDACTED TEXT]
OTH / ADDR AS OF 10-18-99: [REDACTED
TEXT] AKA: ZACK RAYMOND P*
IDENTIFYING INFORMATION: SEX:
MALE*HAIR: RED* EYES: GRN* HT:
6-03*WT: 280* . . . RESTR: MUST WEAR
CORRECTIVE LENSES WHEN DRIVING,
ORGAN AND TISSUE DONOR: NO
UPDATED: 10-20-10 LICENSE STATUS:
VALID* DEPARTMENTAL ACTIONS:
NONE CONVICTIONS: NONE FAILURES
TO APPEAR: NONE ACCIDENTS: NONE
END"

ALLISON TITUS

Office: Building the Library of Water
Stykkishólmur, Iceland

& morning after morning for three weeks straight

we hauled plastic coolers up through the fog

        up to the edge-of-town promontory, to the backdoor

of the former library corrugated

        into the wind & the weather

        reports us kneeling, again, this morning,

up early tucking cloth into the bottom

        of the buckets to archive

& commissary

the rubber mats we trundle, unstack, the rubber tubing we rig to derive

glacier

        from glacier siphoned into rubber jugs, the waters

        named St. Joseph's

        Baby Aspirin, named Bootleg,

        named Broken Settlement Letter,

        named Lighthouse,

we catalogued them

according to our limited apprehension of the parts of native things,

tourists but not tourists

        & therefore not lugging anything

back home. Not returning, but romantically, to the source,
See: jökull slaked westward across oil
cloth in the back of the flatbed we drive

uphill, where we will arrange this new Testimony

of Pitch & Flood, this coastal
tableau we devised, this horse
the color of milk.

Office: Good Stuff Old Dominion Taxidermy

Do it the right way and the prowl gets put
back into the tall grasses behind the tract
houses the highway pins

to the skinny

acres, the less desirable acres. The pelt and
claw get remembered, get to resemble
their former habits of borrow and crawl space

and slink the backyard

landfills for busted deck chairs and wigs
to nest in.

This is how you might resume where you left
off: penmanship tailored to feedlot plus
hitchhike.

This is how the professional mounts the folds
of a leftover body, easing the wood wool
through

the form   removing   the   dead   from its
muscle. Skulk and drove and bone dust
braced in the plaster,

> my poor

pet fox whose eyes, close-up, are so clear, so
bright, the shrubline fixed in the distance of
them   the rabbit's torn up ear

and   pink petals of insulation tufting the ditch
and there, see

the bramble snared
glint of the

noose

held there   hardwired to the nothing that's

left of it.

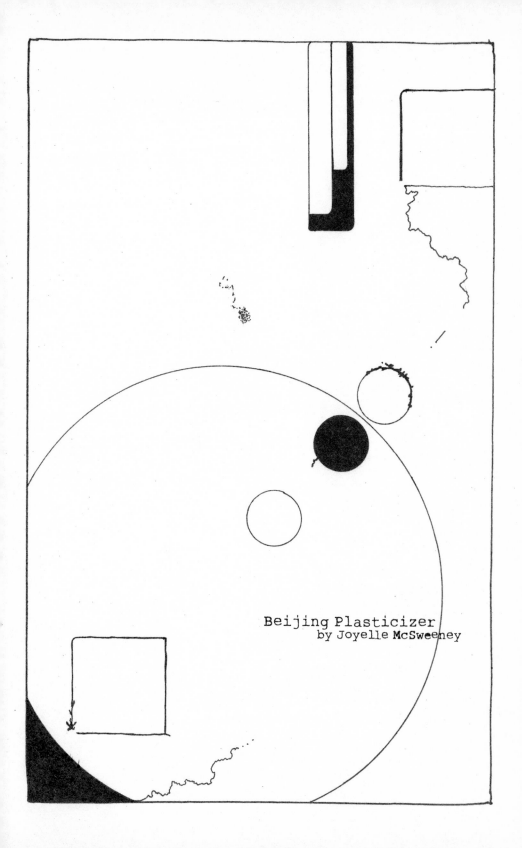

Beijing Plasticizer
by Joyelle McSweeney

Black Beauty

1.
Of all the black beauty
of the Industrial Revolution
this mill was the finest

It shone like a bright camel saddle
through which the needle
must wiggle with its wealth

& now it pushes through.
This scratching of the historical record
releases black vinyl fumes. This virgin refuses

to hold up the roof. She steps out
of her ruined proscenium
waving a scourge

&
lowers it—thwack!—
on history's backside

2.
Black Beauty:
credit where credit is due.
The state collapsing into the arms of the goddess,

debt, a numbered grave, a lower berth, a teenage prostitute
in black vinyl tube top, hemorrhaging
in a chip shop, a beauty, lately shipped in

via container ship, along with 4000 Barbies
& a pail to piss in. What luck
could that container ship contain? Only

irreparable damage:
how the universe signs for its purchases

3.
Then of course when there was less skill required
there was overproduction. Demand
withered up like an old man's.

Curled up like a snail, an antler, a lens,
an olfactory whiff, a fallopian fen,
an irrigation, an embolism, an emblem, a fossile shelf,

a fossile, & a page,
a page, & a caved-in hutch, a hunch,
& a hunch

round a punched-in gut

4.
So the angel tucks up his quirt
climbs off his camel
withdraws into his yurt.

Straps on fish-nets, girdle, stacked heels, then
emerges onto the stage, a ham, complete with cherry
and pineapple ring, one palm

on tassled hip, one
raised into the open disk of light.
His red lip curls
before the hissing microphone. Carcinogens
applaud inside his bones, a phone call

from the future, that ancient

alien home. He croons into the ruins
but can't see them for the light
which brings each stain and blemish to light

5.
Some signs from the print shop:

WHEN THE GUILLOTINE IS IN OPERATION
NO PERSON TO BE WITHIN 1 METRE
OTHER THAN THE OPERATOR.

ENSURE CLAMP AND KNIFE ARE FULLY DOWN

PEN RULING:
THE INKED PENS OF THIS RULING MACHINE.
THE PLAIN PAPER DRAGGED UNDER
THE PENS BY THE CONTINUOUS BELT

GUM ARABIC
AMERI
CAN TYPEWRITER

(The infant on the fairy soap label
is wiped clean of facial features
and other identifying marks—

A perfect victim. Dump her in the fens.
But the type case is full of evidence:
muttons, nut spaces, thicks and hair.)

WITH 26 LEAD SOLDIERS/I HAVE CONQUERED THE WORLD!
Black beauty!

6.
A black letter day.
A gothic script with a grip
on the page.

For the word of God is toothy, fickle, fractious
for a fix. What does He want from us? Wheedling for attention,
riding in his fractal like a rocking-horse moon—

Where the ribs meet, the bosses grin like lozenges
thick with puns and information.
The polyglot bible is full of runes:

A hex for the barn	& a pan for the brain
A pen for the hen	& a blind for the hind
A shot for the pheasant	& a shot for the buck
A shunt for the skull	& a spike for the spine
A cake for the child	& a bar for the hand
A chain for the brain	& a chain for the bicycling heart

For that is a poor heart which
sheds its black robes
& flees its own chambers.

7.
The door unlocks by radar scheme.
Miss Loneliness, Marguerite Duras,
releases her valise and drops wearily to the bed.

Her mug wears lipstick, her cigarette,
stubbed out, wears the slouch and pout
of a gangster's moll, prettily practiced

in the badge of a shot cop. The plot
unreels and reverses itself: refolds
into its envelope but is dropped

into the wet night grass. Whereupon a single rabbit,
like a magician's prop, held aloft by a spangled, aging
beauty, becomes a herd and scales the black hill

as the eye goes compound as a fly's. Black beauty.
A mini-hearse. It lifts off, riffs, carries its blackness
in specks to the sill of the mind. I select

from the wreckage a black valise,
a beauty, its skin rich as a sick
rumour and slick as a dirty mag. I slip

on the ravaged mask of Marguerite Duras,
stitch myself into that fascicle
as into a space capsule. A space age. Even maggots

raised in zero gravity will
abandon that wound
when there's is nothing left to eat,

i.e. dead matter, Marguerite.
Are you grieving? Nah. You pick the locks
again, catch me picking my teeth

with my stiletto. You slice a lighting cue
into my back, breathe lines
into my mouth with your cigarette smoke

& are gone. The locks
snap shut. I finger the brass clasp,
put my ear to the valise,
its chestwall, still ticking,
hear the bony tumblers roll.
I clap the cuff around my wrist, click it shut

& step out into a silhouette so sharp
I could slit the town's throat with it
& do. Black beauty

slicks the sleeping skins.
My name
on everyone's lips.

Plasticizer 1 (flower bomb)

abdominizer, plasticizer,
the flawed flask flushes the brain,
the flash drive inserted
into the correct drain
provides fusion, fluency, the plasticizer
voids the gut, no current can run
anymore thru that florid
fosse, where instinct sinks skindeep,
loses a shoe.
A system should be
made of plastic: too
much beauty crashes the system
with its black drive
a clouding agent sprouts mushrooms
the river flows
underground
where dad wants it: safe in the vein.

A sports drink's
exemplary hue is more vital
-ly electric, more youthful, more energetic, more chemical
-ly pregnant with keys. So teenage model
turns over
with a sigh, unlocks the door
and lets the chain swing, goes back to texting,
compressed
medicinal chest, depreciating values, appreciating
decoration of
the lung with fibrous hues, chinoiserie, capitulation,
capsule view, and I'll no longer be
a capulet, all-day release for all-day releaf,
opheliate, exfoliate in deep debt debut

debrided: particularly
particulate matter now delicately
parting appreciating currently where the skin is pinched
for the stick, wears a blue black
mask and a crown

as milk wears a crown like a bullet when it falls
into film
for the first time, coronated, when it's shot
on camera, spread wide
in the dark room's black corona,
the sun wears a veil of spots, the crowd
varies from itself
in shot after shot,
surges upstream
to the virtual gathering point, now a virtual
viewing platform,
a screen. Continuity breaks
its ribs. Screen says: war is over.
&, how will you spend
your florious dividend?

Plasticizer 2 (sunny era natural life in the city centre)

I do not know which to prefer:
the soft drink in my hand
or the plasticizer which beclouds it

Everybody today is talking about boobs
how they respond to the rubbishy
plasticizer, grow tough rinds and colonies,
capture calories, apply metro-trim,
shuttle commute from the boob to the armpit
to the airport catch
a spring train that barrels through the node,
lymph cells eddy
eject eggy moons

I don't know which to prefer:
the steel bar in my shin
or the human growth hormone festering it
the gingham panty
or the lace that cinches it shut
the seizure in the bone marrow
or spitting into the spittoon
after chemotherapy
or the ingestion of beetle nuts
what infernal ENGINE prototype is this
plasticizer its own grail device search
engine wrapped in wedding veil for the grave
informational overlo
-tion, a
hydrolated
moon shot a wrinkle
into which one hundred plasticizers
may be shot and bloom

(later the stewardess will come through the cabin
to collect used plasticizers)
(More plasticizer = more freedom)
(24-hour plasticizer)

Plasticizer 3 (Land Rover Range Rover)

For trampling the thicket of thick
chiclets clotted cream a dulcet emulsifier
a tranquilizer moon the Emperor Penguin
is dithering over which shoe to spoon
place a goat outside the ladies' quarters with a dish of salt to snuff
poor goat. Dies of salt poisoning. Causing the Emperor
to reel as in a little boat: choice has failed him
and so has chance. Celestial Emperor
Cellular winks sadly to Captive Emperor Penguin from his
tower while the traffic wrinkles lasciviously and squirms.
Between the second and third rings of Saturn you will find
National Rent-a-Car, where you may use your plastic
to rent on credit.

Plasticizer 4 (lamasery)

the clawed pearl has an eye
for the airport iPod
gift shop the Buddha travels
in his own fixed weather it poses
like him on one foot
charming travellers! but erupts
from his golden
abdomen a
fulminous lion
a running sore or
score like
chemo's
scorched earth
policy the flaming
flacial
protrusions
recall a fish
that lives at several
thousand feet on poison
gas a crack
in the c-floor it
takes eyeless snaps by the
mag lite suspended
from the suspension
bridge its brain I mean the lion
wraps the Buddha's
guts like a stomacher
feminizer
fertilizer
run-off fanged and
flanged green roof holds
the industrial slash
imperial waiver which waves inside

the shelving for
ever and
ever in boarding
gate
amen so that fate
becomes dependent on
what is withdrawn
from view Ring on you
orangina
phonebooth
-s hunched and hemi
spheric
engine the lion
makes the inside
the outside the outside
the inside and
on fire

like a plasticizer.

Plasticizer 5 (china post)

O I don't want your ricochet love your
ricochet ricochet I don't want your
bedroom community sleeper cell
cowboy grave love compact
stereo effect don't
want your ricochet boneless peerless meme chose
chanel clutch purse agony play
bonkers Majorca choker tour jeté I
don't want your aquabomberstrut which just
slays everyone
on the dance floor silts
the throat of the channel with a grin
gold gash vermillion mud molar crown identified
by her dental records sigh
when they made you they broke
the chain a broken record
right two times a day
in the universe which breeds and breaks
big bangs don't want
your ricochet
detritus bang
detonate
or residue
bang swab test your pink
bang termination
slip your
scenic bang rivulet
where the brain liquor crests
your overdraft
your underbet
your string

theory un-
raveled to
festive or
fatal effect—

Plasticizer X (terminal)

O love take me back
to your treaty port

My thousand-eyed aircraft
falls like a jewel
into your white petrolatum

My plastic tentacle
retracts

A White Message

for Baoerjinna

1.

On the black page, white writing.
In the white grain, a black secret.
On the white form, a black question.
In the white dress, a white flaw.
In the black beauty, a wrecked current.
In the black river, a white conviction.
In the black bread, a white louse.

2.

The grain is opened. A white
rumor spills from the gap.
It makes a black gesture. Its brow is black.
Why did you born me if you weren't going to love me.
Why did you born me and treat me like that.
Black brain in a white humor.
White laugh in a black mouth.
Black trench in a black forest.
White fissure in a white organ.
White organ in a white soup.
White canal in a black city.
Black instrument in a white circus.
White pain in a black parade.
Lifting my white shinbone split from my skin.

3.

I wear my blackened skin like a garment.
I wear my crownlet of thoughts like a coronet.
I am a carriage pulled by black horses.
Black is my emblem, black my signature.
When my servant blows the trumpet, it makes a white sound
that cleaves open the hearts of my citizens

their white dreams rise from the square
the black blood of doves.

4.
One camera is the commandant.
One camera is the camp.
Another camera enters
with an army of cameras.
Every camera is reeling.
Except for the cameras too tired to reel.
Those cameras are filmed by the others.
The running film goes green with disgust
like a running wound.
But soon even this film is cut and dried.
From the projection booth,
light leaps through the film's windows
but cannot die.
Again and again it leaps from the windows
& is made to leap again.

5.
In the black bread white river.
In the white louse black blood.
In the white hand black writing.
In the black page black secret.
In the black wire black current.
In the black current white horse-eye
rolled back studies white socket.
Rolled back watches white film.
In white film death eyeopen
black awning for a black business.

6.
White moon empties her white stomach
onto the hunched shoulders
of the pines.

Contributors

LEON BAHAM is from the Inland Empire and now lives in Seattle. He is a cross-genre writer whose interests include athletes, celebrities, sacred and lost texts, his mother, cartoons and repressed or gentle violence.

LILLIAN-YVONNE BERTRAM was raised in Buffalo, New York. Her first book, *But a Storm is Blowing from Paradise,* is forthcoming from Red Hen Press in 2012. Her poems have appeared or are forthcoming in *Alligator Juniper, Bellingham Review, Callaloo, Cream City Review, Gulf Coast, Harvard Review, Indiana Review, jubilat, Mid-American Review, Narrative Magazine, OH NO, Rhino, Subtropics,* and *The Walrus.*

JOELLE BIELE is the author of *White Summer* (Southern Illinois) and the editor of *Elizabeth Bishop and The New Yorker: The Complete Correspondence* (Farrar, Straus, and Giroux).

BLAIR BOURASSA is a Canadian who won first place for fiction in the Summer Literary Seminar's 2011 Unified Literary Contest. He studied linguistics at the University of Regina in Saskatchewan, and has lived and worked in many different countries around the world, including Brazil, China, Germany, and Mexico. He has self-published six books, and is currently teaching English at a medical school in Jeddah, Saudi Arabia. More information about him can be found on his personal website at www.voiceinthewilderness.eu.

ESVIE COEMISH is a poet and painter living in St. Johns, Michigan. Currently Esvie is working on a book-length series of love letters, some of which may be found in *Vallum, Main Street Rag, 32 Poems, The Bitter Oleander,* and *Seneca Review.*

SARAH ROSE ETTER'S chapbook, *Tongue Party,* was published by Caketrain Press in May 2011. Her work has appeared in *The Collagist, elimae, Painted Bride Quarterly* and more. You can find her at www. sarahroseetter.com.

DAN GEORGE is a graduate of the College of Santa Fe in Santa Fe, New Mexico, where he studied with Dana Levin. His work has appeared in *LIT, Colorado Review* and is forthcoming in *The American Poetry Review.*

LEE MILENA GOODMAN attended Sarah Lawrence College, and received her MA and MFA from the University of Chicago and CSU Long Beach, respectively. "Barter System" was originally a 2010 finalist in the California Writers Exchange hosted by *Poets & Writers;* she is thrilled to have it printed in *Black Warrior Review.* Her work can be also found in *PANK* and *The Literary Bohemian.* She lives in California.

JP GRITTON is an associate lecturer in creative writing at the Johns Hopkins University. His fiction, journalism, and poetry have appeared in such journals as *Juked, Thieves Jargon,* and *In These Times.*

DEREK GROMADZKI is an MFA candidate and PhD student at the University of Iowa.

ELIZABETH HALL lives in Los Angeles where she works as a private investigator. She is currently finishing her first nonfiction book, *I HAVE DEVOTED MY LIFE TO THE CLITORIS,* a study of small things. She is an associate editor for Les Figues Press.

BRANDON DAVIS JENNINGS lives in Kalamazoo, Michigan, with his fiancée, Tina, and their puppy, Finn MacCool. When he's not working on novels, essays, and stories, he is a PhD candidate in fiction at Western Michigan University. His work has been published in *Crazyhorse, The Berkeley Fiction Review,* and *Curbside Splendor.*

DAWN LONSINGER is pursuing a doctorate at the University of Utah, and is the author of two chapbooks, *the linoleum crop* (Jeanne Duval Editions) and *The Nested Object* (Dancing Girl Press). Her work has recently appeared or is forthcoming in *Another Chicago Magazine, Colorado Review, Guernica, Subtropics* and *The American Poetry Review*. She, like most living organisms, has a thing for light.

CHRISTINA MANWELLER lives in Colorado, where she writes poetry and nonfiction. Her work has appeared in various journals in the US, Canada and Ireland, most recently in *Creative Nonfiction*.

FARID MATUK is the author of *This Isa Nice Neighborhood* (Letter Machine, 2010), which earned honorable mention in the Arab American Book Award and was a finalist for the Norma Farber First Book Prize from the Poetry Society of America. His poems have appeared most recently in *6x6, Third Coast, The Boston Review,* and online at *Esque* and *Everyday Genius*. He currently serves on the editorial team at *Fence*. Matuk lives in Dallas with his wife the poet Susan Briante and their daughter.

EDGAR MCHERLY draws comics at invisiblehairsuit.com.

JOYELLE MCSWEENEY is the author of *The Necropastoral* (Spork Press) a collection of essays and poems featuring collages by Andrew Shuta; two hybrid novels, *Flet* (Fence Books) and *Nylund, the Sarcographer* (Tarpaulin Sky Press); and two books of poetry, *The Red Bird* and *The Commandrine and Other Poems*, both from Fence. She is a co-founder of Action Books and *Action Yes,* a press and web-quarterly for international writing and hybrid forms, and a founding contributor of *Montevidayo,* a collective blog for hi- lo- pop-culture. The poems in this chapbook are from *Percussion Grenade: Poems and Plays,* forthcoming from Fence in Spring 2012. A book of prose, *Salamandrine: 8 Gothics,* is forthcoming from Tarpaulin Sky Press in Fall 2012.

HELEN PYNOR is a contemporary artist working primarily in photography, sculpture and installation. Her work explores the experience, perception, and representation of the interior body, looking for alternative languages to the use of gore and horror, or clinical neutrality. Pynor's practice has included exhibitions, residencies and commissions in Australia, Asia and Europe and she has been the recipient of several prestigious national awards in Australia. She recently completed a PhD at Sydney College of the Arts, The University of Sydney, and she holds a Bachelor of Visual Arts (Sydney College of the Arts) and a Bachelor of Science (1st class honours) (Macquarie University). Pynor currently lives and works in London.

KATHLEEN ROONEY is a founding editor of Rose Metal Press, a non-profit dedicated to the publication of literary work in hybrid genres. Her most recent books include the essay collection *For You, For You I Am Trilling These Songs* (Counterpoint, 2010) and the poetry chapbook, *After Robinson Has Gone* (Greying Ghost Press, 2011).

ZACHARY SCHOMBURG is the author of *The Man Suit* (Black Ocean, 2007), *Scary, No Scary* (Black Ocean, 2009), and two forthcoming books, *Fjords* and *The Book of Joshua*. He co-edits *Octopus Magazine* and Octopus Books. He lives in Portland, Oregon.

BRANDON SHIMODA was born in California, and has lived most recently in Maine and Taiwan. He is the author of three books—*The Girl Without Arms* (Black Ocean, 2011), *O Bon* (Litmus Press, 2011) and *The Alps* (Flim Forum, 2008).

NICK ST. JOHN came from a small town in California. He is currently traveling and making comics, more of which can be seen at nickstjohn.net. He may need to sleep on your couch at some point if that's okay.

SHELLY TAYLOR is the author of *Black-Eyed Heifer* (Tarpaulin Sky Press, 2010), which was named one of the top 30 poetry books of 2010 by *Coldfront Magazine*. *Peaches the yes-girl* (Portable Press at Yo-Yo Labs, 2008) and *Land Wide to Get a Hold Lost In* (Dancing Girl Press, 2009) are her two chapbooks.

ALLISON TITUS' first book, *Sum of every lost ship*, is available from CSU Press; new poems have most recently appeared in *A Public Space* and *Gulf Coast*, and in 2010 she was awarded a poetry fellowship from the NEA. She lives and works in Richmond, Virginia.

JA TYLER is the author of *A Man of Glass & All the Ways We Have Failed* and has recent work with *Diagram, Redivider, Fourteen Hills,* and *New York Tyrant.* He is also founding editor of Mud Luscious Press. For more, visit: www.chokeonthesewords.com.

KAREN VOLKMAN's three books of poetry are *Crash's Law, Spar,* and *Nomina.* She teaches at the University of Montana in Missoula.

AFTON WILKY is an avid believer in doing what she's not s'posed to. She adores being shocked by brilliance and is the Poetry Editor at *NDRMag.* Her work has also appeared in *BlazeVOX.*

JOY WOOD received an MFA in fiction from the University of Michigan, where she was a Zell Postgraduate Fellow in Creative Writing. She has been awarded residency fellowships from the Santa Fe Art Institute and the MacDowell Colony, and her work is forthcoming in *Glimmer Train.* She is the managing editor of *Guernica.*

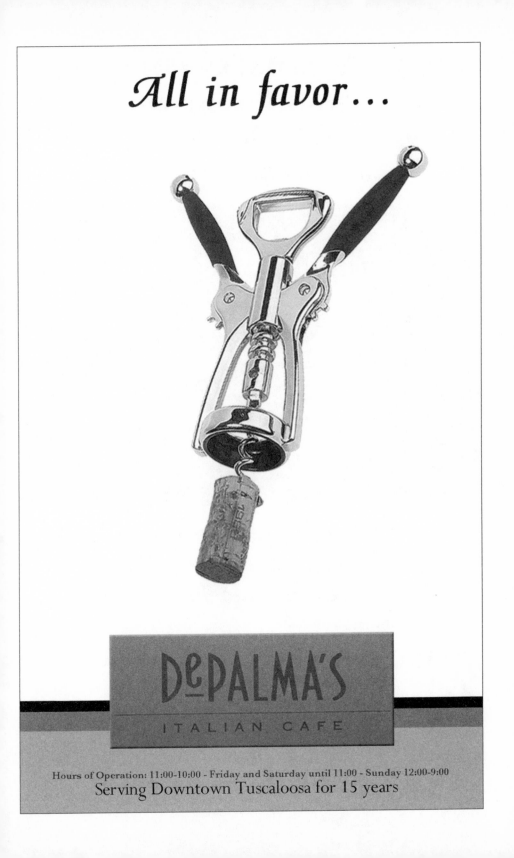

MFA in the Book Arts

John Sirmon and Kerri Harding work on 100% cotton handmade papers in the Lost Arch Papermill.

The Master of Fine Arts (M.F.A.) in the Book Arts Program in the School of Library & Information Studies at The University of Alabama is now in its twenty-seventh year. The 60-credit-hour program emphasizes the craft and art of books including *bookbinding, letterpress printing, hand papermaking,* and *the history of the book.* Our highly motivated students come from varied undergraduate backgrounds and life experiences. We have a number of graduate assistantships and fellowships available yearly on a competitive basis. To find out more about the Alabama program please contact Steve Miller, The University of Alabama, School of Library & Information Studies, Box 870252, Tuscaloosa, AL 35497-0252, stevemiller@bookarts.ua.edu.

Our website features over 100 *podcast interviews* of amazing book artists (or search for *Book Artists and Poets* on iTunes), video from some of our *bookmaking trips to Cuba,* as well as *current news* about the program. Visit us at www. bookarts.ua.edu.

THE UNIVERSITY OF
ALABAMA
CREATIVE WRITING REWRITTEN

RESIDENT FACULTY
Robin Behn
Joel Brouwer
Dave Madden
Michael Martone
Wendy Rawlings
Peter Streckfus
Kellie Wells
Patti White

Visit the web site for details on our guaranteed financial support and the Capote Fellowships; our innovative curriculum; our engaged & accessible faculty; our eclectic & committed student body; the Black Warrior Review, one of the country's premier literary journals; our students' and graduates' books, national awards & job placements; our Bankhead Visiting Writers Series; our Coal Royalty chairholders; and the lively local culture.

www.bama.ua.edu/~writing

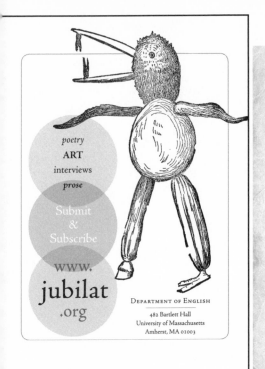
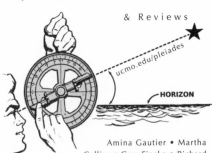

Egan's Bar

THICK SMOKE, DIM LIGHTS, LOUD MUSIC.

OPEN MONDAY-
THURSDAY, SATURDAY
2PM - 2AM
FRIDAY 2PM - 3AM
SUNDAY 2PM - 9:30PM

HOME OF THE
HALF-SHOT

COLDEST BEER
AROUND

Egan's Bar

THICK SMOKE,
DIM LIGHTS,
LOUD MUSIC.

OPEN MONDAY-
THURSDAY, SATURDAY
2PM - 2AM
FRIDAY 2PM - 3AM
SUNDAY 2PM - 9:30PM

FRIENDLIEST
STAFF IN TOWN

BEST PLACE TO
WATCH THE NFL

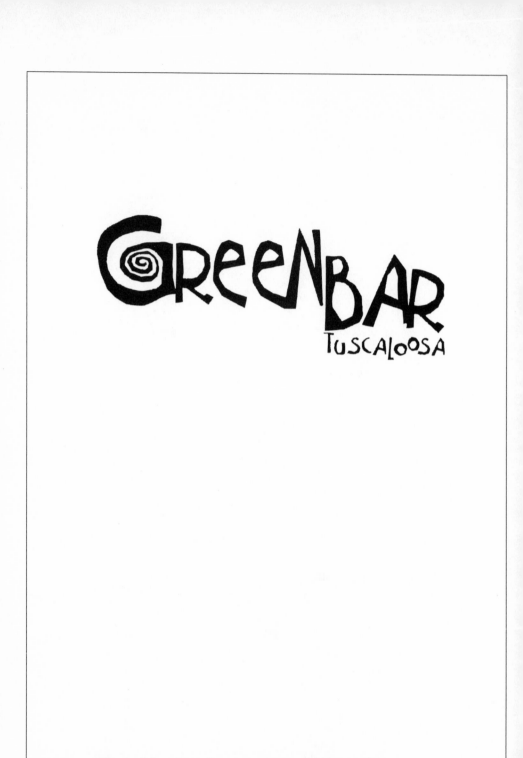

KENTUCK

40 Days of Celebration

40 Days of Kentuck Blog Kick Off *September 7*
5K Run & Block Party *September 9*
Kentuck for Kids Coloring Book Reception *September 14*
a la cARTe: Linda Munoz 40th Anniversary mosaic bench project *September 17*
Art Night: Kentuck Tree Challenge & Festival Quilts exhibit *October 6*
Larry Godwin exhibit and ceremony unveiling plaque honoring Rusty the dog *October 1*
Kentuck Festival Patron Party *October 14*
Kentuck Festival Artist Party *October 15*
40th Annual Kentuck Festival of the Arts *October 15 & 16*

www.kentuck.org 205-758-1257 kentuck@kentuck.org 503 Main Avenue Northport, AL 35476

THE STATE'S PREMIER LITERARY NETWORK

ALABAMA

AWF

WRITERS' FORUM

A partnership program of
The Alabama State Council on the Arts

P.O. Box 4777, Montgomery, AL 36103-4777
334-265-7728 • Toll Free: 866-901-1117
www.writersforum.org

The editors gratefully acknowledge the generosity of the following friends of
Black Warrior Review:

Fine Arts Committee of the Leadership Board of the College of Arts and Sciences
Department of English
Office of Student Media
Media Planning Board
The Blount Foundation

The editors also thank J. Clemson Duckworth for establishing the Susie B. Duckworth Endowed Support Fund
and for his ongoing contributions, which provide payment to the writers and artists whose work appears in *Black
Warrior Review*.